GCSE Physics

The Workbook

This book is for anyone doing **GCSE Physics**.

It's full of **tricky questions**... each one designed to make you **sweat** — because that's the only way you'll get any **better**.

There are questions to see **what facts** you know. There are questions to see how well you can **apply those facts**. And there are questions to see what you know about **how science works**.

It's also got some daft bits in to try and make the whole experience at least vaguely entertaining for you.

What CGP is all about

Our sole aim here at CGP is to produce the highest quality books — carefully written, immaculately presented and dangerously close to being funny.

Then we work our socks off to get them out to you — at the cheapest possible prices.

Contents

Published by Coordination Group Publications Ltd.

Editors:
Sarah Hilton, Kate Houghton, Ali Palin, Katherine Reed, Rachel Selway, Laurence Stamford, Sarah Williams, Julie Wakeling.

Contributors:
Steve Coggins, Mark A Edwards, Dr Giles R Greenway, Jason Howell, Frederick Langridge, Barbara Mascetti, John Myers, Richard Parsons, Andy Rankin, Pat Szczesniak, Paul Warren, Jim Wilson.

ISBN: 978 1 84146 644 6

Groovy website: www.cgpbooks.co.uk

Printed by Elanders Hindson Ltd, Newcastle upon Tyne.
Jolly bits of clipart from CorelDRAW®

Moving and Storing Heat

Q1 Complete these sentences by circling the correct word from each pair.

Heat is a measure of **hotness** / **energy**.

Temperature is a measure of **hotness** / **energy**.

Heat travels from a **hot** / **cold** place to a **hot** / **cold** place.

Water is a good material for storing heat because it has a **high** / **low** specific heat capacity.

When a substance is heated its particles vibrate **more** / **less** quickly.

Q2 **Temperature** can be measured on various **scales.**

a) Give an example of a scale used to measure temperature. ....

b) Everyday **temperature** scales go **lower than zero**. Explain why it isn't possible to have a measurement of **heat** that is below zero.

....

....

Q3 a) What is **specific heat capacity?**

....

b) Agatha has 1 kg samples of two substances — A and B. Substance **A** has a **higher** specific heat capacity than substance B. Both samples cool down by 10 °C. Which will release more heat — A or B? Circle the correct answer.

Substance A

Substance B

Q4 Mildred thinks she could make her hot water bottle more efficient by filling it with **mercury**, which has a specific heat capacity of **139 J/kg°C**. The specific heat capacity of water is **4200 J/kg°C.**

Work out the **difference** in energy released by two litres of mercury cooling from 70 °C to 20 °C and two litres of water cooling from 70 °C to 20 °C .
(2 l of mercury have a mass of 27.2 kg. 2 l of water have a mass of 2 kg.)

....

....

....

....

Q5 A piece of copper is heated to **90 °C** and then lowered into a beaker of water which is at **20 °C.** The copper transfers **3040 J** of energy to the water before it is removed. The temperature of the copper after it is removed is **50 °C.** The specific heat capacity of copper is **380 J/kg°C.**

Calculate the **mass** of the copper. ....

....

Melting and Boiling

Q1 The graph shows the temperature change as a substance is heated up. The letters A to E represent each **state** of the substance and each **change of state**.

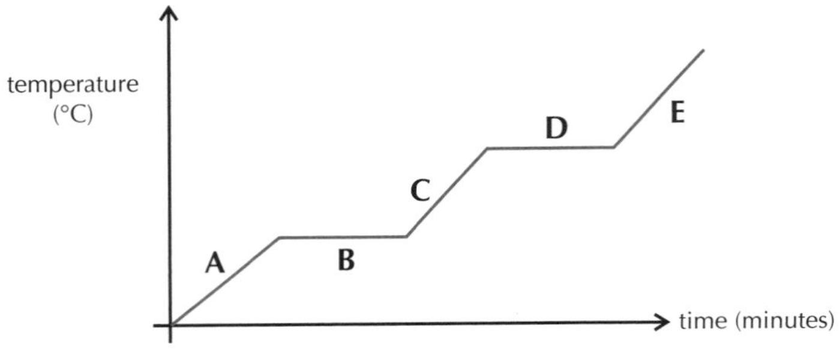

Boiling	A
Gas	B
Liquid	C
Melting	D
Solid	E

Draw lines to join each state or change of state to the correct letter.

Q2 A beaker of pure water is heated. When it reaches 100 °C it **stays** at 100 °C, even though it is **still being heated**. Which of sentences A-D is the correct explanation for why this happens? Circle the correct letter.

A Energy is being lost to the surroundings as quickly as it is being supplied to the beaker.

B The pan is absorbing the extra energy.

C The energy supplied is used to break intermolecular bonds and change the water to steam.

D A more powerful heater should have been used.

Q3 The graph shows what happens to the temperature of a beaker of **molten wax** as it cools to room temperature.

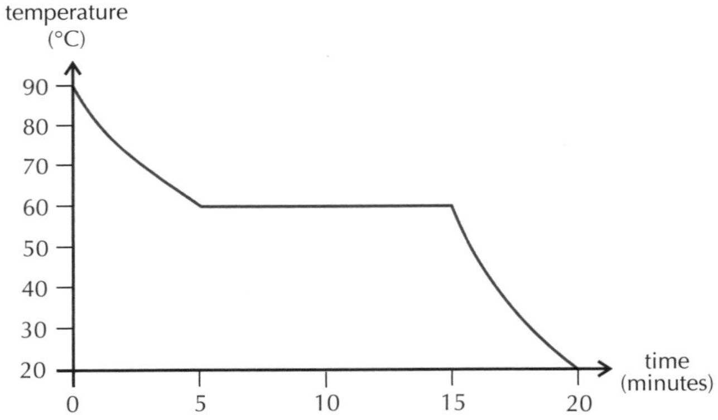

a) At what temperature does the wax become **solid**?

....

b) Explain why the temperature of the wax **remains constant** during solidification.

....

....

c) **How long** after the start of the experiment was it before all the liquid wax became solid again?

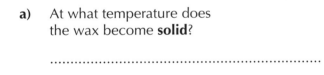

....

Melting and Boiling

Q4 A kettle supplies energy at a rate of **2500 J per second**. It contains 1.5 litres of water which is at 100 °C. **How long** would the kettle need to boil for in order to **evaporate** all this water? (The specific latent heat of water for boiling is 2.26 MJ/kg. 1 litre of water has a mass of 1 kg.)

....

....

....

Q5 Answer the following questions using the information in the table.

Substance	Melting Point (°C)	Specific latent heat of melting (kJ/kg)
Water (ice)	0	334
Aluminium	658	321
Copper	1083	176
Lead	327	224
Zinc	419	118

a) A heater supplies **500 kJ** of thermal energy over **10 minutes**.

i) Use the table to calculate the **mass of ice** at 0 °C that it could melt in 10 minutes.

....

....

ii) Use the table to calculate the **mass of zinc** at 419 °C that it could melt in 10 minutes.

....

....

b) Dave puts **ice** in his lemonade to cool it down. The ice melts.
Calculate the energy transferred to **30 g** of ice cubes by **300 g** of lemonade as the ice melts.

....

....

Top Tips: Don't get mixed up between **specific heat capacity** and **specific latent heat**. Remember that changes of state mean staying at the same temperature for a while.

Conduction and Convection

Q1 Indicate whether the sentences are **true** or **false**.

	True	False
a) Conduction involves energy passing between vibrating particles.	☐	☐
b) Some metals are very poor conductors.	☐	☐
c) Solids are usually better conductors of heat than liquids and gases.	☐	☐
d) Plastic is a poor conductor because it contains free electrons.	☐	☐

Q2 George picks up a piece of wood and a metal spoon. Both have the same temperature: 20 °C.

Explain why the metal spoon feels **colder** to the touch than the piece of wood.

....

....

Q3 Jamie wears cotton vests in summer but string vests in winter. He always wears the same kind of shirt.

Jamie finds that a string vest keeps him warmer than a cotton vest. Why is this?

....

....

Q4 Match each observation with an explanation.

The very bottom of a hot water tank stays cold...

Warm air rises...

A small heater can send heat all over a room...

because water doesn't conduct much heat.

because heat flows from warm places to cooler ones.

because it is not so dense.

Q5 Sam uses the apparatus shown to investigate heat transfer in water.

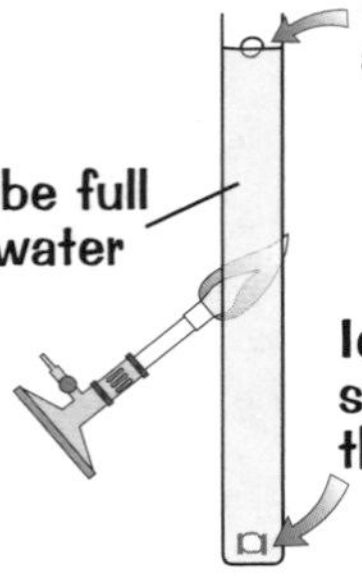

He heats the middle of the tube with a Bunsen flame. The ice at the top of the tube melts quickly but the ice at the bottom does not melt.

What does this experiment show about conduction and convection in water? Explain your answer.

....

....

....

Heat Radiation

Q1 a) Indicate whether each of the following statements is **true** or **false**.

	True	False
i) Heat radiation is sometimes called infrared radiation.	☐	☐
ii) Hot objects do not absorb radiation.	☐	☐
iii) Cold objects do not emit radiation.	☐	☐

b) Write out corrected versions of the **false** statements.

....

....

....

Q2 Three flasks, each containing 100 ml of water, are placed in closed boxes. The water in the flasks and the air in the boxes are at different temperatures as shown.

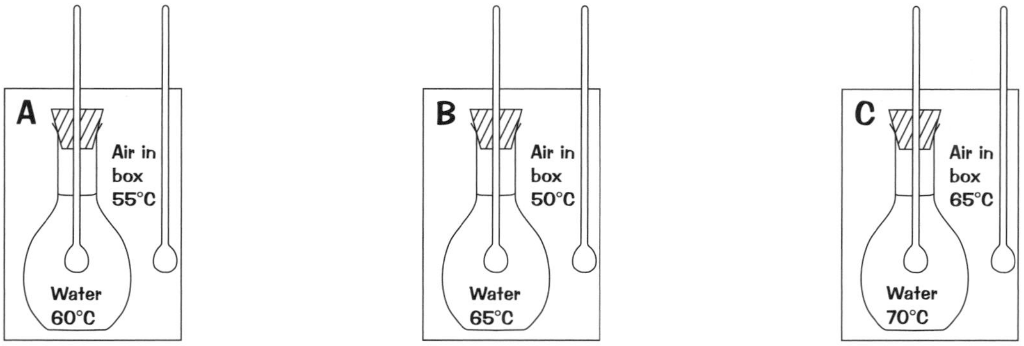

Which flask will cool fastest? Give a reason for your answer.

Flask .... will cool fastest because ....

....

Q3 Two pupils are talking about how we get heat energy from the Sun.

Peter:
The Sun warms the Earth by convection.
Lucy:
The Sun warms us because it is much hotter than the Earth.

For each pupil, circle whether they are right or wrong and explain your answer.

a) Peter is right / wrong because

....

b) Lucy is right / wrong because

....

Heat Radiation

Q4 Tick the correct boxes below to show whether the sentences are **true** or **false**.

		True	False
a)	The amount of heat radiation absorbed by a surface depends only on its colour.	☐	☐
b)	The hotter a surface is, the more heat it radiates.	☐	☐
c)	Good absorbers of heat are also good emitters of heat.	☐	☐
d)	Thermos flasks can keep hot things hot but cannot keep cold things cold.	☐	☐
e)	Silver survival blankets help the body to absorb heat.	☐	☐

Q5 Tim did an investigation using a **Leslie's cube**. Each surface on the cube had a different combination of **colour** and **texture** as shown.

Tim measured the heat radiation coming from each surface. His results are shown below.

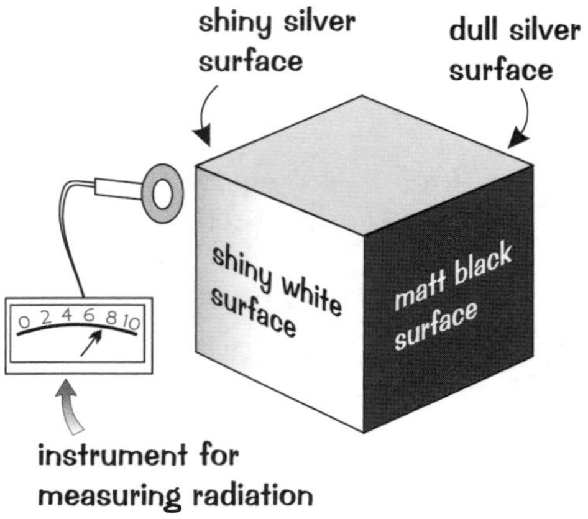

Surface	Reading	Colour and Texture
A	10	
B	4	dull silver
C	4	
D	2	

a) Complete the table to show which surface — A, B, C or D — was:

i) the **matt black** surface. **ii)** the **shiny silver** surface. **iii)** the **shiny white** surface.

b) Which of the surfaces A to D would be best for the following applications? Explain your answers.

i) The outside of an electric kettle.

....

....

ii) The outside of a refrigerator.

....

....

....

iii) The cooling fins on a car engine.

....

....

Saving Energy

Q1 On the diagram, write down one type of insulation which could be installed to reduce heat losses through the roof, walls and doors of a house.

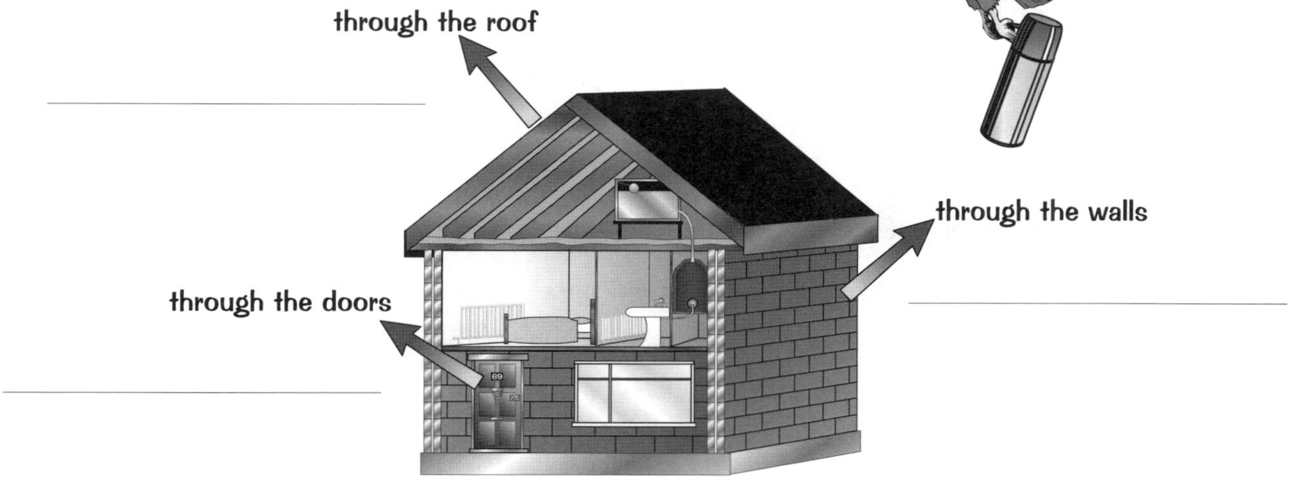

Q2 Mr Tarantino wants to buy **double glazing** for his house, but the salesman tries to sell him insulated window shutters instead. He says it is cheaper and more **cost-effective**.

	Double glazing	Insulated window shutters
Initial Cost	£3000	£1200
Annual Saving	£60	£20
Payback time	50 years	

a) Calculate the **payback time** for insulated shutters and write it in the table.

b) Is the salesman's advice **correct**? Give reasons for your answer.

....

....

c) Suggest two other measures Mr Tarantino could take to reduce heat losses through the windows.

....

Q3 Explain how the following types of insulation work.

a) Cavity wall insulation ....

....

b) Loft insulation ....

....

Energy Transfer

Q1 Complete the following **energy transfer diagrams** to show the energy inputs and useful energy outputs. The first one has been done for you.

A solar water heating panel: light energy → heat energy

a) A gas cooker: .... → heat energy

b) An electric buzzer: electrical energy → ....

c) A television screen: .... → ....

Q2 Use the words below to fill in the gaps.

conservation   run out   stay the same   resources   principle

The word .... has two very different meanings related to energy. It can mean using fewer energy .... so that they don't .... It can also mean the .... that the total amount of energy in the Universe will always ....

Q3 The diagram shows a **steam locomotive.**

a) What form(s) of energy are there in the:

i) coal ....

ii) hot steam (which powers the engine) ....

b) Describe two **energy transfers** which take place on the locomotive.

1. ....

2. ....

Q4

Bruce is practising weightlifting.

a) When Bruce holds the bar still, above his head, what kind of energy does the weight have?

....

b) Bruce had porridge for breakfast. Describe how the chemical energy in his porridge is converted to the gravitational potential energy of the lifted bar.

....

....

c) When Bruce lets go of the weight, what happens to its energy?

....

Energy Transformation Diagrams

Q1 This diagram shows the energy changes in a **toy crane**. The diagram is drawn to scale.

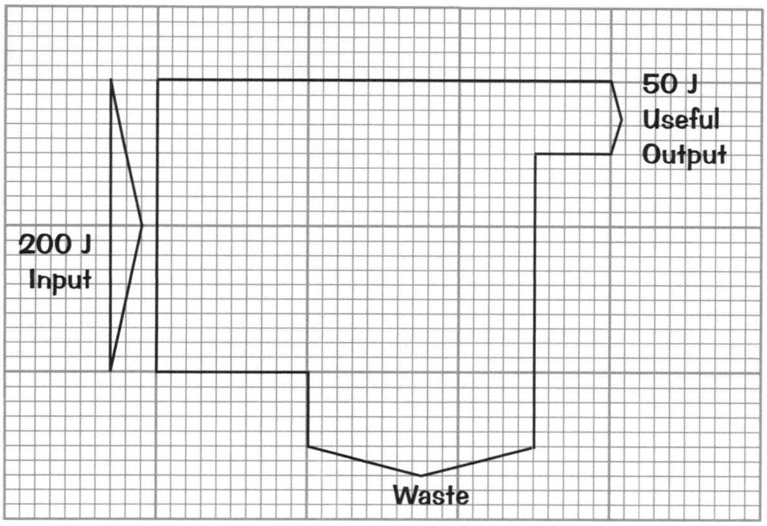

a) How much energy is **one small square** worth? .... J

b) How much energy is **wasted**? .... J

Q2 Professor Bean is testing a new **high-efficiency** car engine.
He finds that for every 100 J of energy supplied to the engine, 75 J are transformed into **kinetic energy** in the moving car, 5 J are wasted as **sound energy** and the rest is turned into **heat energy**.

On the graph paper below, draw an **energy transformation diagram** to illustrate his results.

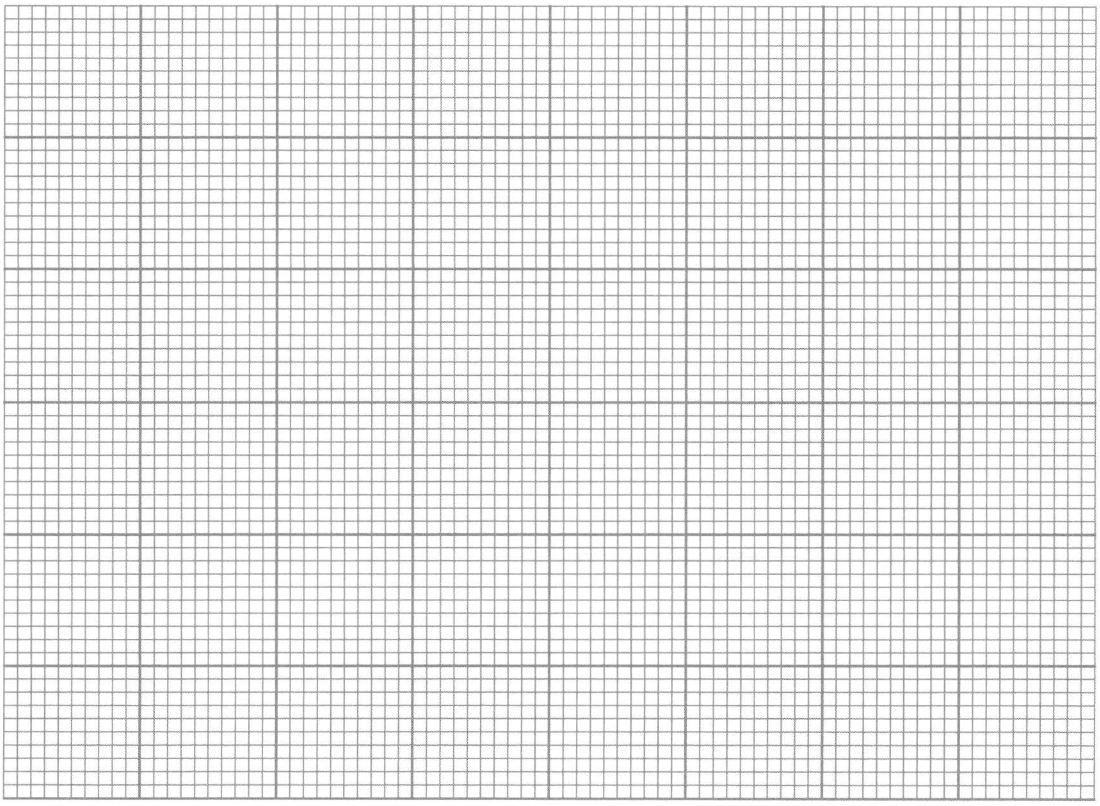

Energy Transformation Diagrams

Q3 Liam measured the energy input and outputs for a model **electrical generator**. He drew this diagram to show his results.

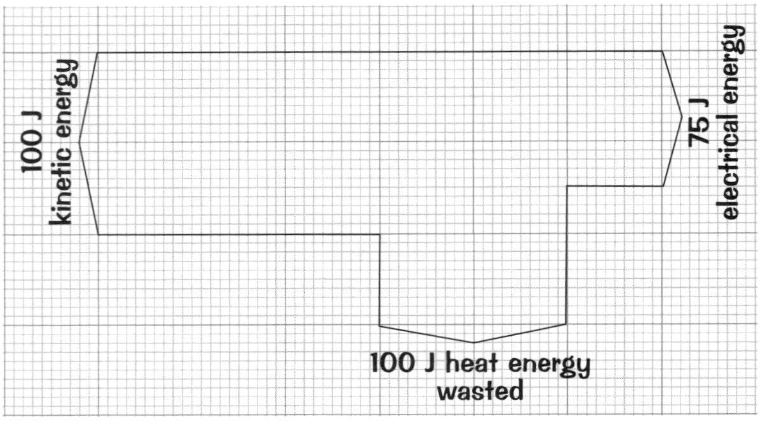

Describe two mistakes Liam has made on his diagram, and suggest how to correct them.

1. ....

....

2. ....

....

Q4 The Sankey diagram below is for a **winch** — a machine which **lifts** objects on hooks and cables.

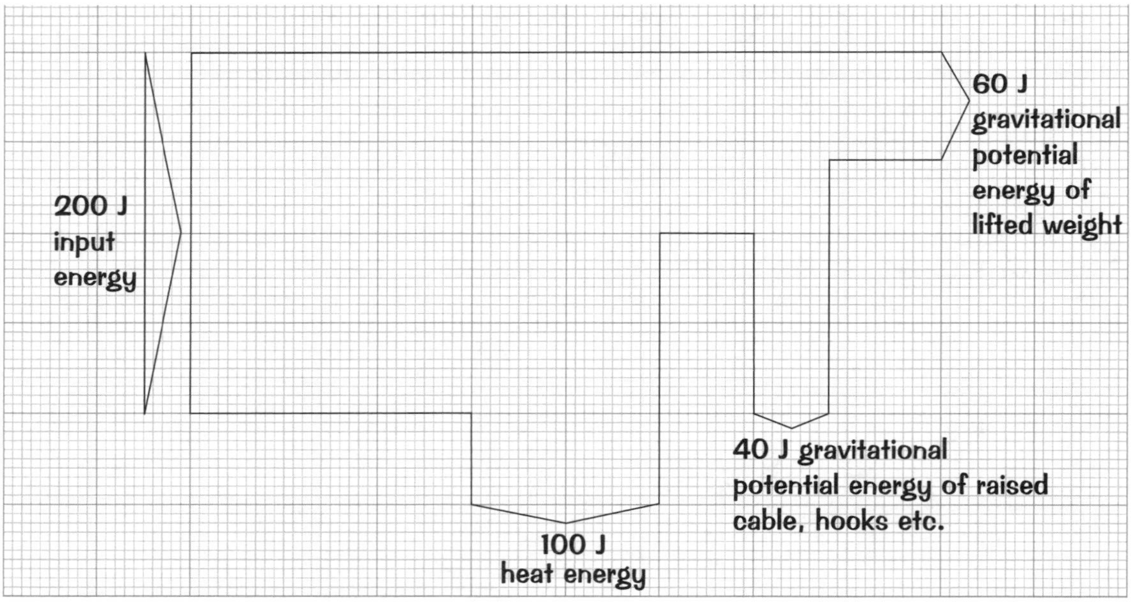

a) What is the total amount of energy **wasted**? .... J

b) How much useful **gravitational energy** is produced? .... J

c) Calculate the **efficiency** of the winch. Give your answer as a decimal.

Efficiency = Useful Energy Output ÷ Energy Input

....

....

Efficiency

Q1 Fill in the gaps by choosing words from the list below.

heat	light	input	create	output	total	useful	fraction	convert

Most **machines** are devices which .... energy from one form to another. Some of the energy supplied to the machine is converted into .... output energy. But some energy is always wasted — often as .... energy. The **efficiency** of a machine is the .... of the **total energy** .... that is converted into useful energy ....

Q2 Here is the **energy flow diagram** for an electric lamp.

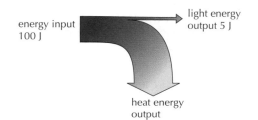

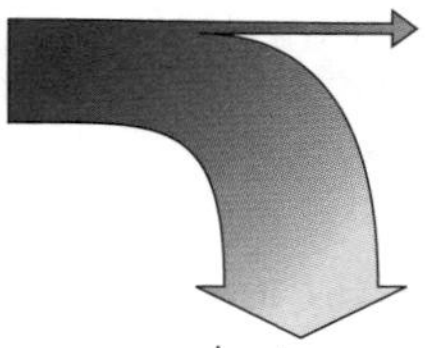

a) The total **energy input** is .... J

b) The **useful energy output** is .... J

c) The amount of energy **wasted** is .... J

d) The efficiency of the bulb is .... %

Q3 Use the **efficiency formula** to complete the table.

Total Energy Input (J)	Useful Energy Output (J)	Efficiency
2000	1500	
	2000	0.50
4000		0.25
600	200	
	500	0.20
200		0.90

Q4 Tina was investigating a model **winch** — a machine that uses an electric motor to lift objects.

Tina calculated that, in theory, **10 J** of electrical energy would be needed to lift a **boot** 50 cm off a table. She then tried lifting the boot with the winch and found that **20 J** of electrical energy was actually used.

Why did the winch use so much electrical energy in practice?
In your answer, include an explanation of what happened to the 'extra' 10 joules.

....

....

Energy Sources

Q1 Most of the UK's electricity is generated using **non-renewable** energy resources.

a) Explain the difference between 'renewable' and 'non-renewable' energy resources.

~~non~~ renewable will never run out but non-renewable will.

b) From those given below, **circle** the renewable resources and **underline** the non-renewables.

coal waves natural gas hydroelectric wind oil

tidal solar biomass nuclear geothermal

Q2 Using non-renewable energy sources can cause many environmental problems.

a) Match up each environmental problem below with something that causes it.

Acid rain	releasing CO_2 by burning fossil fuels
Climate change	coal mining
Dangerous radioactive waste	sulfur dioxide formed by burning oil and coal
Spoiling of natural landscapes	using nuclear power

b) Why is most of our energy generated from non-renewable sources despite the damage this causes?

They provide a lot of energy, they are reliable and easy to use

Q3 Most of our energy comes indirectly from the **Sun.**

a) Explain how the Sun is the ultimate source of the energy in:

i) biomass ....

ii) waves ....

b) State which energy sources do **not** originate in the Sun and explain where they come from.

....

Nuclear and Geothermal Energy

Q1 Each of the following sentences is incorrect. Write a correct version of each.

a) A nuclear reactor uses radon to make heat.

....

b) Nuclear power stations are cheaper to build than coal fired power stations and quicker to start up.

....

Q2 State two **advantages** of nuclear power over fossil fuels.

....

....

Q3 Outline two **disadvantages** of using nuclear power.

....

....

Q4 **High-level** radioactive waste is **harder** to dispose of than low-level waste.

a) High-level nuclear waste is disposed of by burying it deep underground.
What two steps are taken before burying the waste?

1) ....

2) ....

b) Scientists have to find suitable sites to bury high-level nuclear waste.
Why must sites for disposal of high-level waste be geologically stable?

....

....

Q5 Tick the boxes to show whether these statements about **geothermal** energy are true or false.

	True	False
a) Set-up costs are low.	☐	☐
b) The heat is produced by radioactive elements.	☐	☐
c) It is possible in any country in the world.	☐	☐
d) There are lots of associated environmental problems.	☐	☐

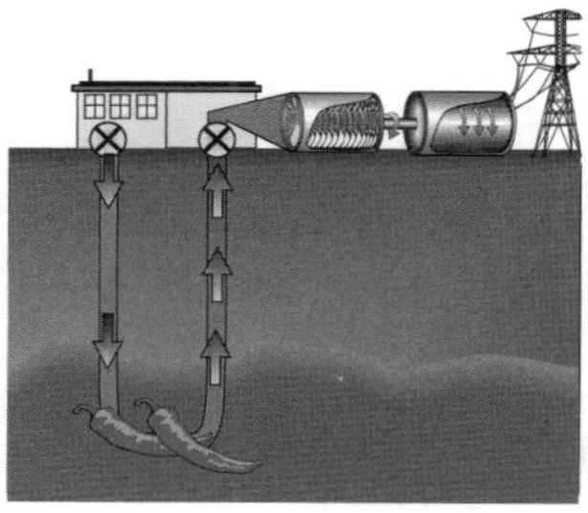

Wind and Solar Energy

Q1 People often object to wind turbines being put up near where they live.

a) Give two reasons why they might object.

1) ....

2) ....

b) Give two arguments in favour of using wind turbines to generate electricity.

1) ....

2) ....

Q2 Choose from the words below to complete the passage about how **solar cells** generate electricity. Each word may be used once, more than once, or not at all.

semiconductor metal atoms neutrons DC protons AC electrons silicon

Solar cells are usually made of ...., which is a .... When sunlight falls on the cell, silicon .... absorb some of the energy of the light, knocking some of their .... loose. These .... then flow around a circuit as a .... current.

Q3 Explain the advantages and disadvantages of using **solar cells** to generate electricity.

....

....

....

Q4 The diagram shows a **passive solar heating panel**.

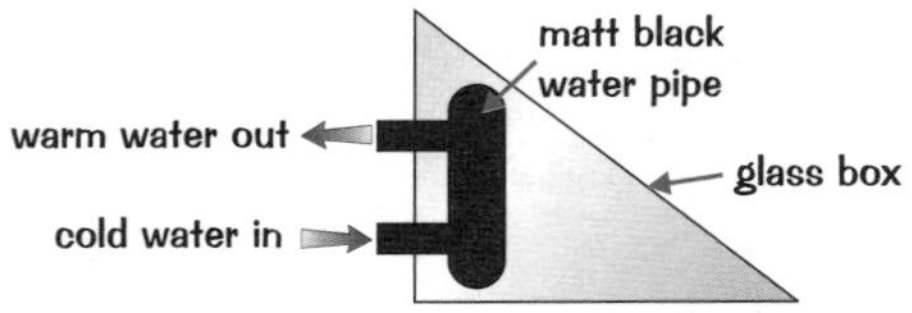

a) **i)** Why is the water pipe matt black?

....

ii) Why is the water pipe inside a glass box?

....

b) A solar panel can be made to track the position of the Sun in the sky. Why is this done?

....

....

Biomass, Wave and Tidal Energy

Q1 Tick the boxes to show whether each statement applies to **wave** power or **tidal** power or **both**.

		Wave	Tidal
a)	Is usually used in estuaries.	☐	☐
b)	Suitable for small-scale use.	☐	☐
c)	Is a reliable way to generate electricity.	☐	☐
d)	The amount of energy generated depends on the weather.	☐	☐
e)	The amount of energy generated depends on the time of the month and year.	☐	☐

Q2 **Tidal barrages** can be used to generate electricity.

What happens to make turbines go round?

a) Explain how a tidal barrage works.

....

....

....

b) Give two reasons why people might object to a tidal barrage being built.

1. ....

2. ....

Q3 **Wave-powered generators** can be very useful around islands, like Britain.

a) Number these sentences 1 to 6, to explain how a wave-powered generator works.

☐ The spinning generator makes electricity.

☐ The moving air makes the turbine spin.

☐ The water goes down again.

☐ Air is sucked downwards, spinning the turbine the other way and generating more power.

☐ A wave moves water upwards, forcing air out towards a turbine.

☐ The spinning turbine drives a generator.

b) Give two possible problems with using wave power.

1. ....

2. ....

Biomass, Wave and Tidal Energy

Q4 Chicken droppings are an example of **biomass.**

a) Describe how electricity can be generated from chicken droppings.

....

....

b) Explain why chicken droppings are a renewable source of energy.

....

c) Give two other examples of biomass which could be burned to generate electricity.

....

d) Explain why burning biomass is 'carbon neutral'.

....

....

Q5 Mr Saleem is a cattle farmer in India.
He has just installed a small **biogas** plant on his farm.

a) What is meant by 'biogas'?

....

b) What source of biogas is Mr Saleem likely to use?

....

c) Apart from cooking and heating, how else could Mr Saleem make use of the biogas?

....

Q6 Fiza and Julie are discussing the environmental impacts of burning **landfill rubbish** to generate electricity.

Fiza says: **"Burning rubbish gives off harmful gases."**

Julie says: **"But it's better than just burying your rubbish and burning coal instead."**

Who do you think is right? Explain your answer.

....

....

Top Tips: Burning animal poo is nothing new — people have been doing it for years, and many still do. For instance, if you're a nomadic yak herder in Mongolia, you probably don't have **mains electricity**, but you **do** have lots of **yak poo**. Dry it, burn it, and you'll have a nice warm tent.

Hydroelectric and Pumped Storage

Q1 These sentences explain how pumped storage works. Put them in the right order by numbering them 1 to 4.

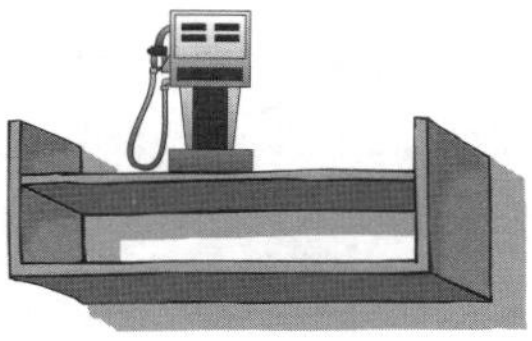

- [ ] Water at a high level stores energy until it is needed.
- [ ] At peak times water is allowed to flow downhill, powering turbines and generating electricity.
- [ ] At night big power stations make more electricity than is needed.
- [ ] Spare electricity is used to pump water from reservoirs at a low level to others at a high level.

Q2 Match up the beginnings and ends of the sentences. In one case, two matches are possible.

Big coal-fired power stations deliver energy...	when it is needed.
Pumped storage power stations deliver energy...	all the time.
Hydroelectric power stations deliver electricity...	that they have previously stored.

Q3 At a public meeting, people are sharing their views about hydroelectric power.

We should use hydroelectric power more — it doesn't cause any pollution.
And it gives us loads of free energy.
But it makes a terrible mess of the countryside.
At least it's reliable — it always gives us electricity when we need it.
Brian
Hillary
Sue
Liz

Say whether you agree or disagree with each person's view, and explain your reasons.

a) I **agree** / **disagree** with Brian because ....

....

b) I **agree** / **disagree** with Hillary because ....

....

c) I **agree** / **disagree** with Sue because ....

....

d) I **agree** / **disagree** with Liz because ....

....

e) Outline one **advantage** of hydroelectric power which was not mentioned at the public meeting.

....

Electric Current

Q1 Use words from the list to complete the passage below.
You may need to use some words more than once.

protons	electrons	resistance	voltage	current

Current is the flow of .... around a circuit. Current flows through a component which has a .... across it.
The size of the current depends on the size of the .... and on how much .... there is.

Q2 The flow of electricity in circuits can be compared to the flow of water in pipes.

a) In a water 'circuit', what is the equivalent to electrical **current**?

....

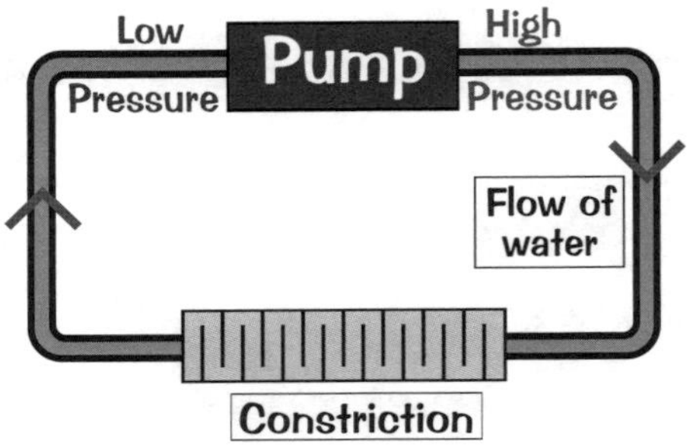

b) If there is a water pump in the system, what electrical device does it correspond to?

....

c) What corresponds to electrical **resistance** in a water 'circuit'?

....

d) The pump is turned up. Explain what happens to the flow of water.
What would the equivalent action be in an electrical circuit?

....

Q3 Draw a trace that a cathode ray oscilloscope might show if it was displaying the current from:

a) the mains electricity supply

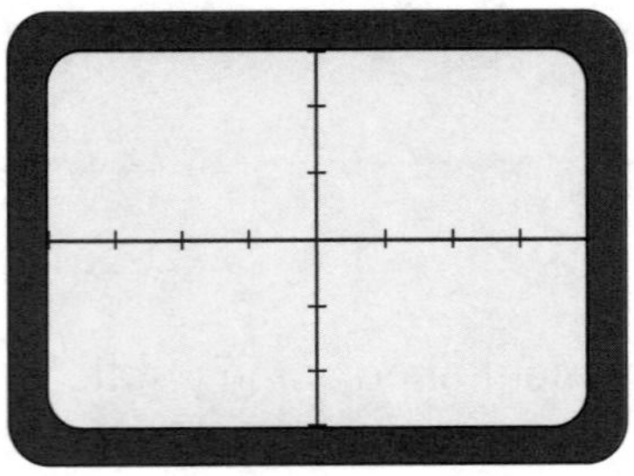

b) a battery

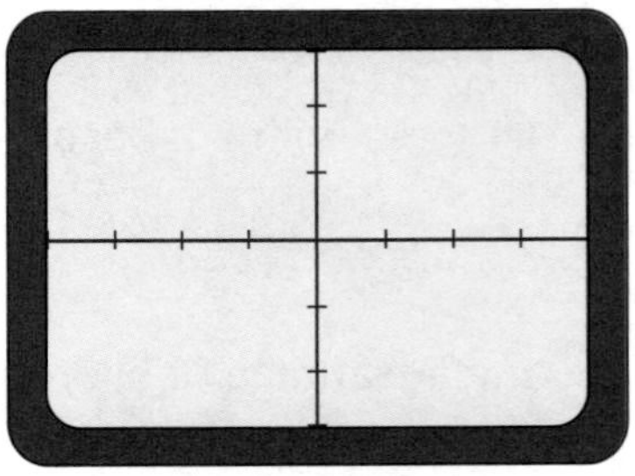

Current, Voltage and Resistance

Q1 Complete these sentences by circling the correct word from each pair.

a) Increasing the voltage **increases / decreases** the current that flows.

b) If the voltage is kept constant, increasing the resistance **increases / decreases** the current that flows.

Q2 Fabio sets up a standard circuit using a **variable resistor** to test the resistance of a material.

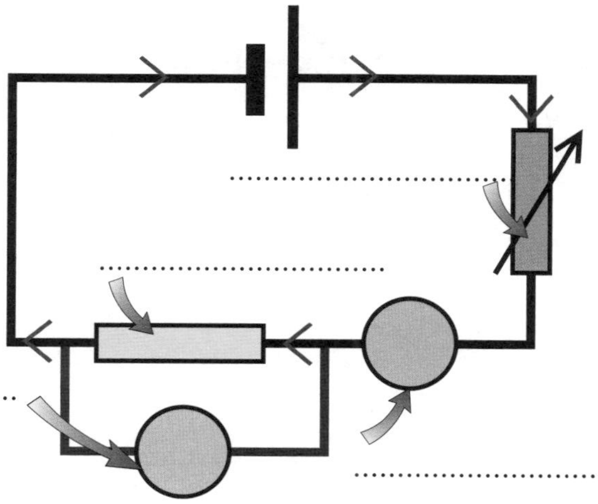

a) Label the standard test circuit components using the words in the box below.

voltmeter	material
variable resistor	ammeter

b) Fabio sets the variable resistor at its minimum resistance. He measures a current of 2.4 A and a voltage of 6 V. Calculate the resistance of the material.

Make sure you use the right units.

....

c) How would Fabio use the variable resistor to help get a reliable result from his experiment?

....

....

....

Q3 Fill in the missing values in the table below.

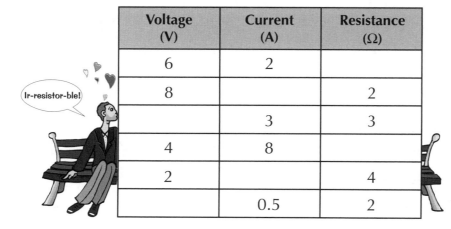

Voltage (V)	Current (A)	Resistance (Ω)
6	2	
8		2
	3	3
4	8	
2		4
	0.5	2

The Dynamo Effect

Q1 Look at the apparatus shown in the diagram below.

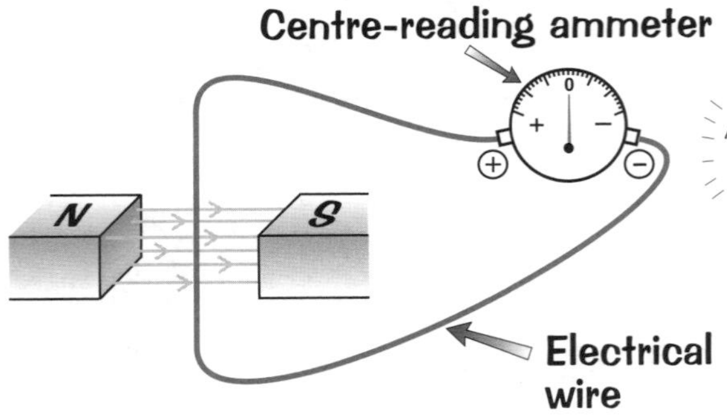

Electromagnetic induction is sometimes called the generator effect.

a) Describe how you could use the apparatus to demonstrate electromagnetic induction.

....

....

....

b) What you would see on the ammeter? ....

....

c) What effect, if any, would the following have on the ammeter reading:

i) swapping the magnets

....

ii) reversing the connections to the ammeter

....

Q2 A simple **dynamo** can be made by rotating a magnet end to end inside a coil of wire.

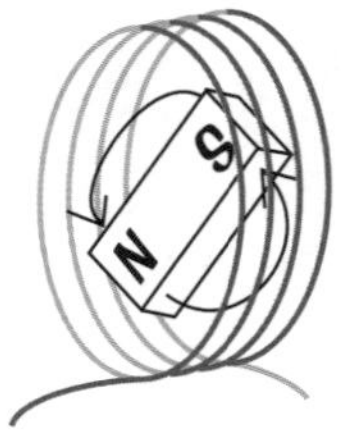

a) What happens to the magnetic field when the magnet turns half a turn?

....

b) What is created in the wire by this rotation?

....

c) The magnet is constantly turned in the same direction.
Would this generate an AC or DC current in the wire?

....

The Dynamo Effect

Q3 Moving a **magnet** inside an **electric coil** produces a trace on a cathode ray oscilloscope.

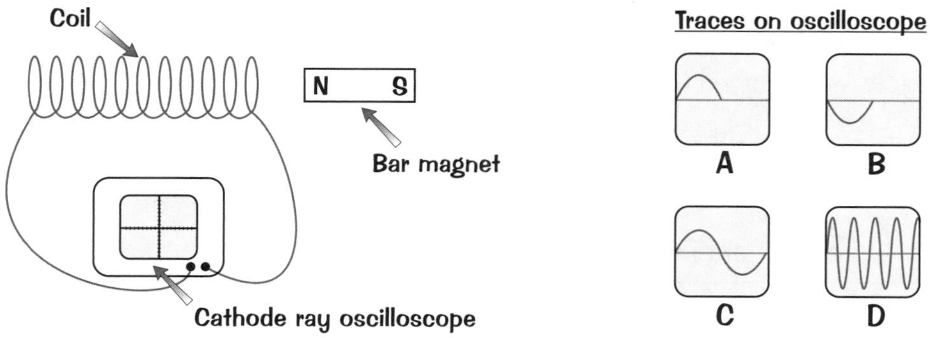

When the magnet was pushed inside the coil, trace A was produced on the screen.

a) Explain how trace B could be produced.

....

b) Explain how trace C could be produced.

....

c) Explain how trace D could be produced.

....

d) Explain how energy is transferred from the moving magnet to the oscilloscope.

....

Q4 Look at the simple **AC generators** sketched below.

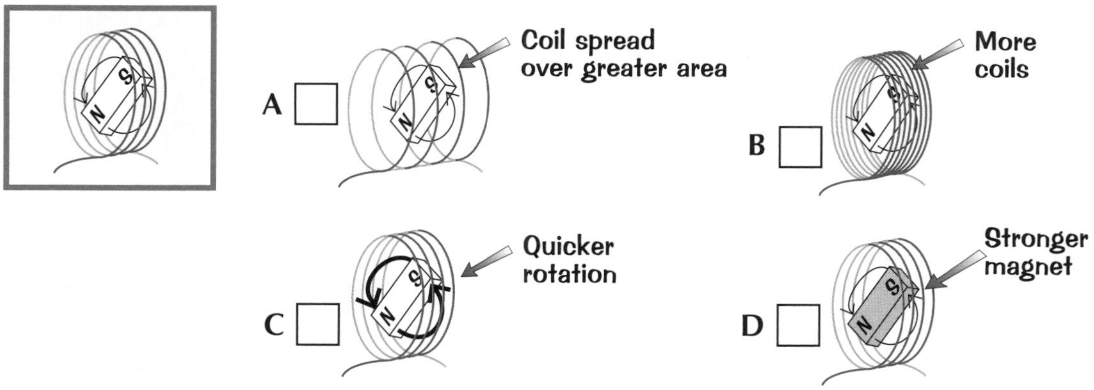

One of the generators labelled A – D will **not** induce a higher voltage than the generator in the box. Tick the appropriate box.

Top Tips: Electromagnetic induction is a very **useful** bit of Physics — it's how we make all our electricity. The massive generators in a power station and the tiny whirring dynamo on my bike both work in the same way — you either turn a conductor in a magnetic field (that's a generator) or rotate a magnet near a conductor (a dynamo). The principle is the same for both — there's a **conductor** experiencing a **changing magnetic field**, and the result is an **induced voltage**.

Power Stations and the National Grid

Q1 Complete the passage by choosing from the words given.

National	Express	Grid	power stations	worms	farms	consumers	generated

Most electricity is produced by .... The ....
.... is the network of pylons and cables which covers the whole country.
It enables electricity .... almost anywhere to be supplied to
.... almost anywhere, e.g. homes and ....

Q2 In a large **power station** there are several steps involved in making electricity. Number these steps in the right order — from 1 to 5.

- ☐ Hot steam rushes through a turbine and makes it spin.
- ☐ Electricity is produced by the spinning generator.
- ☐ A fossil fuel such as coal is burned to release heat.
- ☐ The spinning turbine makes the generator spin too.
- ☐ Water is heated in the boiler and turned to steam.

Q3 Each of the following sentences is **incorrect**. Write out a correct version of each.

a) The National Grid transmits energy at high voltage and high current.

....

b) A step-up transformer is used to reduce the voltage of the supply before electricity is transmitted.

....

c) Using a high current makes sure there is not much energy wasted.

....

Q4 At full working speed a **generator** in a power station turns **50 times per second**.

a) What type of electrical current is supplied by the generator — **AC** or **DC**?

....

b) Explain how this type of current allows the voltage of the supply to be stepped up or down.

....

....

Electrical Power

Q1 The **current** an appliance draws depends on its **power** rating. Complete the table below, showing the power rating and current drawn by various appliances at mains voltage — **230 V**.

Appliance	Power (W)	Current (A)
Kettle	2600	
Radio	13	
Laptop computer		3.2
Lamp		0.17

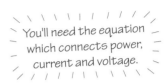

You'll need the equation which connects power, current and voltage.

Q2 Boris puts his **2 kW** electric heater on for **3 hours**.

a) Calculate how many **kilowatt-hours** of electrical energy the heater uses.

.... kWh.

b) Boris gets his electricity supply from Ivasparkco. They charge 7p per kilowatt-hour. Work out the **cost** of the energy calculated in part (a).

....

....

c) Boris's wife grumbles at him for leaving a 60 W lamp on overnight — about 9 hours every night. Boris says his wife uses **more energy** by using an 8 kW shower for 15 minutes every day.

Is Boris right? Calculate how much energy each person uses and compare your results.

....

....

....

Q3 Mr Havel recently received his **electricity bill**. Unfortunately, he tore off the bottom part to write a shopping list.

Customer : Havel, V

Date	Meter Reading
11 06 06	34259
10 09 06	34783

Total Cost @ 9.7p per Unit

a) How many **Units** of energy did Mr Havel use in the three months from June to September?

....

b) What would the bill have said for 'total cost'?

....

....

Waves

Q1 Diagrams **A**, **B** and **C** represent electromagnetic waves.

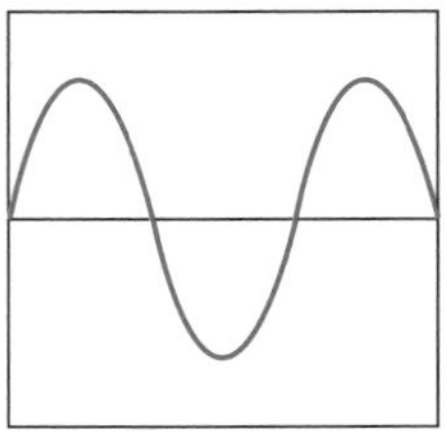

A

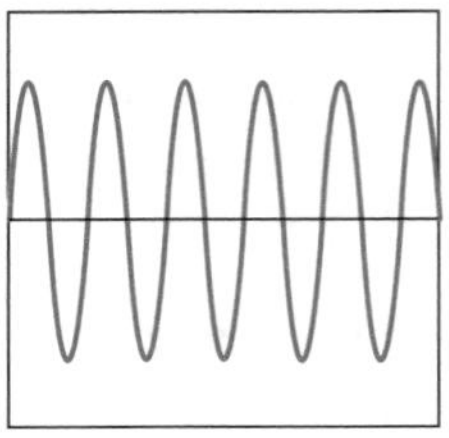

B

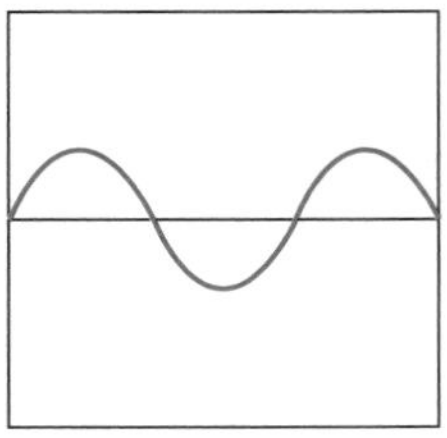

C

a) Which two diagrams show waves with the same **frequency**? .... and ....

b) Which two diagrams show waves with the same **amplitude**? .... and ....

c) Which two diagrams show waves with the same **wavelength**? .... and ....

Q2 Tick to show whether the following statements are **true** or **false**.

	True	False
a) Visible light travels faster than both X-rays and radio waves.	☐	☐
b) All EM waves transfer matter from place to place.	☐	☐
c) Radio waves have the shortest wavelength of all EM waves.	☐	☐
d) The amplitude of a wave is measured from trough to crest.	☐	☐

Q3 Which of the phrases below relate to **transverse** waves and which to **longitudinal**? Write '**T**' for transverse, and '**L**' for longitudinal.

☐ vibrations are at 90° to the direction of travel of the wave

☐ electromagnetic radiation

☐ sound waves

☐ vibrations are along the same direction as the wave is travelling

☐ produced by a slinky spring whose end is wiggled at 90° to the spring itself

☐ ripples on water

☐ produced by a slinky spring whose end is pushed and pulled towards and away from the rest of the spring

Q4 Red light and violet light are at the opposite ends of the **visible** spectrum. Describe two things they have in **common** and two ways in which they **differ**.

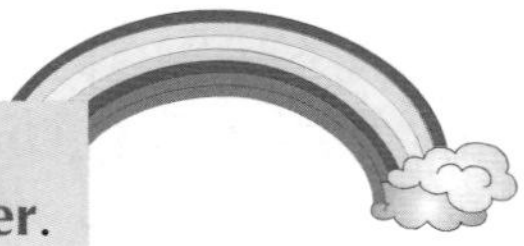

Similarities: 1) ....

2) ....

Differences: 1) ....

2) ....

Waves

Q5 When radio waves meet they **interfere** with one another.
Interference can be constructive or destructive.

a) The diagram below shows two waves combining.
On each of the empty sets of axes, draw what the combined wave would look like.

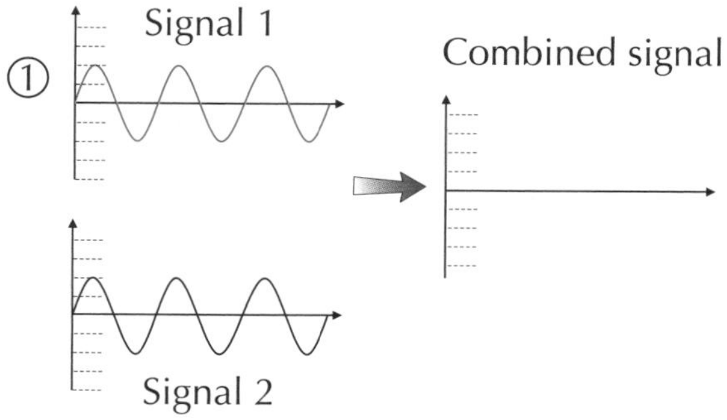

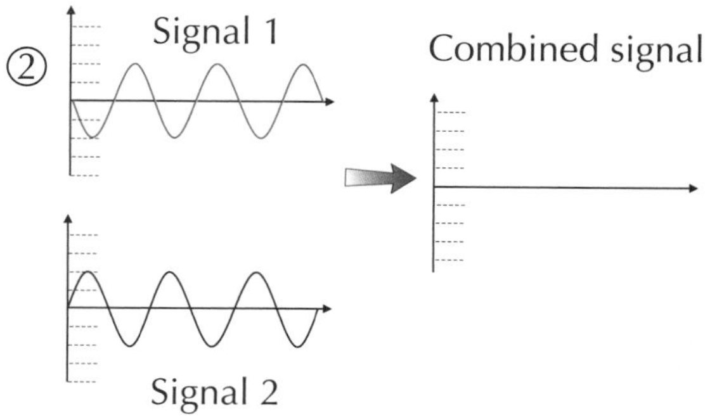

b) Complete the following sentence.

For two waves to completely destructively interfere, they must have the same amplitude, the same .... and they must be .... phase.

c) Rebekah listens to a radio station broadcasting on 1152 kHz.
One day, another radio station starts broadcasting on 1155 kHz.
Suggest why Rebekah's listening experience might be **worse** than before.

....

....

Q6 All EM waves can be **reflected**, **refracted** and **diffracted**.
Draw lines to match each of these three statements to the correct description.

a) Long wave radio waves can bend around **obstacles** such as hills.

b) Your remote control will still work if you point it away from the TV towards a flat solid object, e.g. a plate or saucer.

c) The bottom of a swimming pool looks **nearer** than it actually is.

Reflection

Diffraction

Refraction

Top Tips: EM radiation can be **absorbed** instead of reflected — it just depends on the **wavelength** of the radiation and the type of **material** it's colliding with. Absorption of EM waves can be really handy — it allows your microwave oven to **heat food** using **microwaves**. It also causes **radio waves** to be transformed into **alternating currents** inside your radio.

Refraction

Q1 Diagrams A and B show waves travelling from a **dense** medium to a **less dense** medium.

A
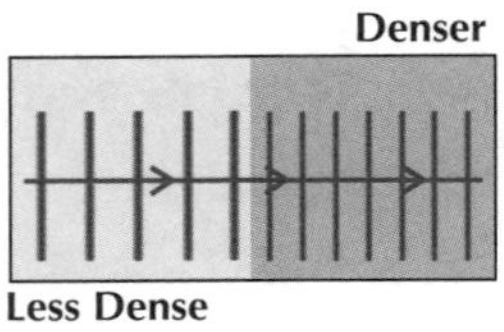

B
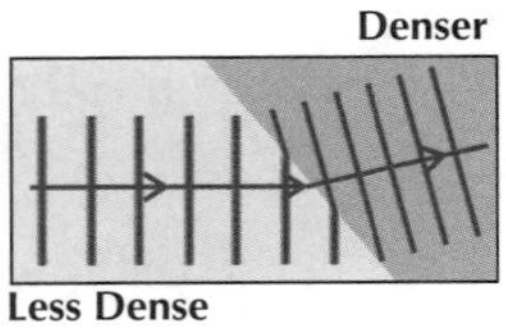

a) Which diagram shows the waves being **refracted**?

....

b) Why does refraction **not happen** in the other diagram?

....

c) What happens to the **wavelength** of the waves after they have passed into a denser medium?

....

d) What happens to the **frequency** of the waves after they have passed into a denser medium?

....

e) What happens to the **velocity** of the waves after they have passed into a denser medium?

....

f) Imagine that the wave in diagram B passed into the **less dense** medium again.
What would happen to the speed of the wave?

....

....

Q2 Doctors can use an **endoscope** to look inside a patient's body. An endoscope has **two** bundles of optical fibres — one carries light down into your stomach, say, and the other returns the **reflected** light back to a monitor.

a) Optical fibres work because of repeated **total internal reflections**.
Complete the ray diagrams below.

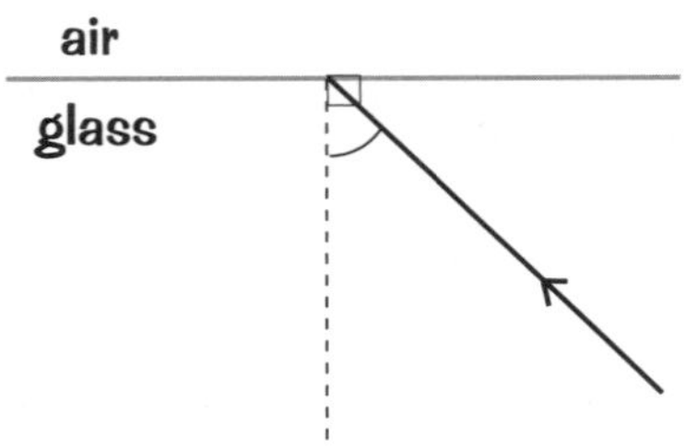

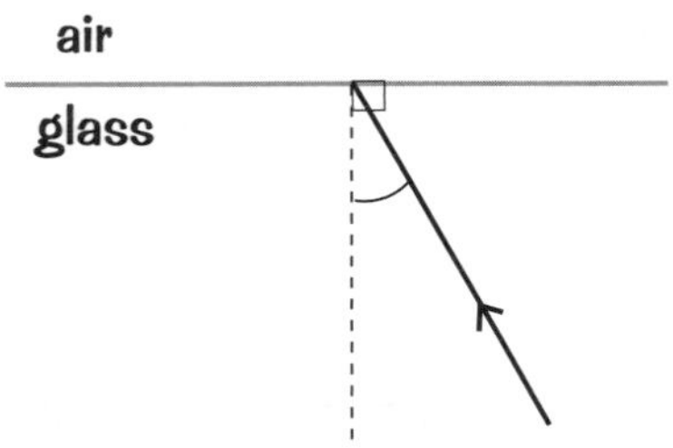

The critical angle for glass/air is 42°.

b) Explain why doctors must be careful not to **bend** an endoscope sharply.

....

Dangers of EM Radiation

Q1 Give two examples of how EM waves can be **helpful** and two examples of how they can be **harmful**.

Helpful: 1) .... 2) ....

Harmful: 1) .... 2) ....

Q2 The graph opposite shows how the **energy** of EM waves varies with **frequency**.

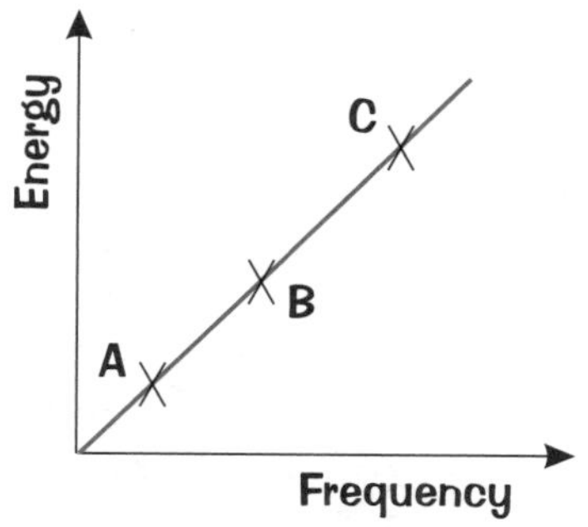

a) What is the mathematical relationship between frequency and energy?

....

....

b) Draw arrows to match points **A**, **B** and **C** on the graph to the three types of radiation below.

green light | gamma radiation | radio waves

A | B | C

Q3 Explain why:

a) It is safe to use fluorescent tubes in lights, even though harmful UV rays are produced inside them.

....

b) Darker-skinned people are less likely to suffer from skin cancer.

....

....

c) Radiographers stand behind lead screens when they are taking X-rays of a patient, even though it's considered an acceptable risk for the patient to be deliberately exposed to X-rays.

....

....

Q4 The **ozone layer** is high up in the atmosphere.

a) How does the ozone layer help **protect** life on Earth?

....

b) Some (now banned) polluting gases break up ozone molecules. What are these gases called?

....

Uses of Waves

Q1 Gabrielle, in London, and Carwyn, in Toronto, are talking by **mobile phone**.

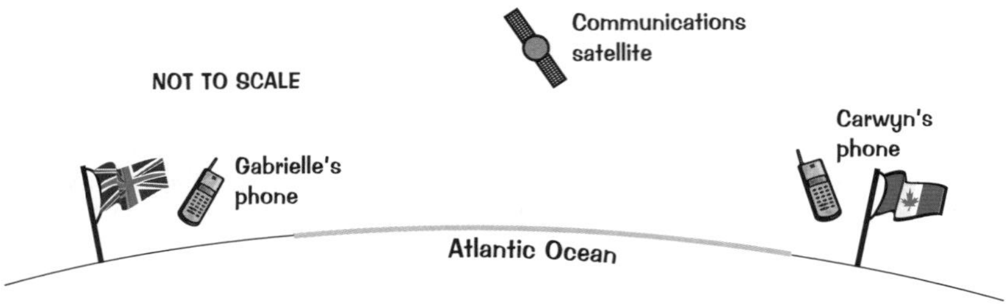

a) Gabrielle's phone sends a signal to a **transmitter**, which sends a signal to the communications satellite. Suggest why Gabrielle's phone doesn't send the signal **straight to the satellite**.

....

b) Carwyn goes into the city centre of Toronto, and finds that her mobile phone sometimes **loses reception** when she walks down streets with a lot of tall buildings.

i) Explain **why** Carwyn's phone loses reception in the city centre streets.

....

....

ii) The nearest transmitter to Carwyn is on a hill 2 miles from her house. Explain **why** the transmitter needs to be on a hill.

....

Q2 Sharon is heating up some ready-made curry in her **microwave** oven.

a) **Briefly explain** how microwaves heat up the curry.

....

....

b) The instructions on the curry packaging say to take the curry out of the microwave and **stir** it half way through the cooking time. Sharon doesn't bother to do this. When she takes the curry out, it's **overcooked** on top, and **undercooked** in the middle. Explain **why** the curry is like this.

....

....

Q3 Choose from the words below to complete this passage about diagnosing fractured bones.

lead **plastic** **bones** **transmitted** **soft tissue** **aluminium** **absorbed**

X-rays can pass easily through .... but are .... more by .... Screens and shields made of .... are used to minimise unnecessary exposure to X-rays.

Uses of Waves

Q4 The diagram shows part of a CD player.

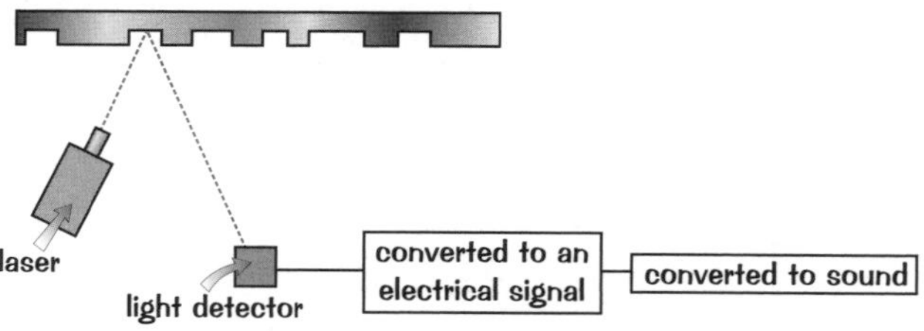

a) Why do CDs have to be **shiny**? ....

b) Describe how information is stored on a CD.

....

....

Q5 Tick the box next to the process that does **not** make use of wave **reflection**.

☐ prenatal scanning ☐ reading a book ☐ iris scanning

☐ a CD player ☐ night vision camera

Q6 Ultrasound scanning can reveal things about a developing foetus.

a) Apart from showing whether a baby is alive, give two pieces of information that can be obtained from an ultrasound scan.

1) ....

2) ....

b) A lot of information that can be found from an ultrasound scan could also be obtained from an X-ray of the mother. Explain why this isn't done.

....

Q7 Below are some sentences about using **iris scans** as a security check. Tick those that are true. **Rewrite** the others to make them true.

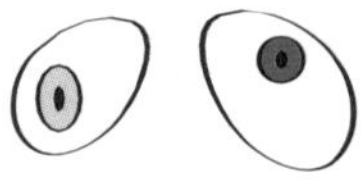

a) A person's iris won't normally change during their lifetime. ☐

....

b) A person's two irises do not match. ☐

....

c) Iris scanners use ultraviolet radiation to form the image of a person's iris. ☐

....

Analogue and Digital Signals

Q1 Fill in the blanks, choosing from the words below.

digital	analogue	amplified	weaken	interference	noise

All signals .... as they travel. To overcome this, they can be .... Signals may also suffer .... from other signals or from electrical disturbances. This causes .... in the signal. When .... signals are amplified, the noise is also amplified.

Q2 Sketch: a 'clean' digital signal. a 'noisy' digital signal. a 'noisy' analogue signal.

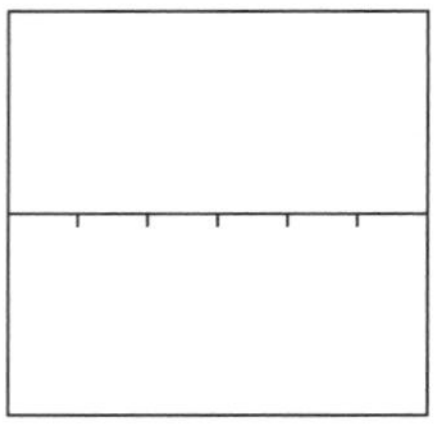

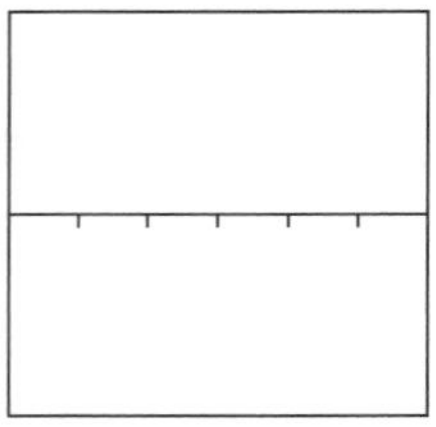

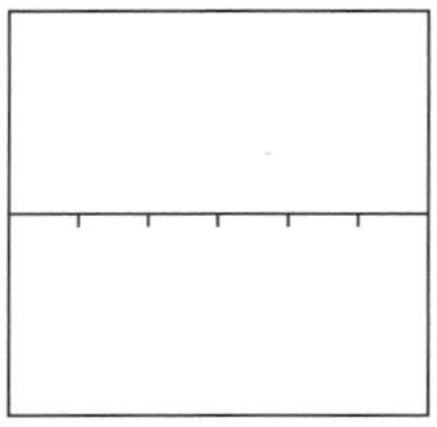

Q3 a) Explain why it is better to send **digital** signals to a computer rather than analogue ones.

....

b) Explain why digital signals suffer less from **noise** than analogue signals.

....

....

c) State one other advantage of using digital signals for communication.

....

Q4 The diagrams opposite show magnified views of the surfaces of a **compact disc** and an old-fashioned **record**.

The CD is read by a laser, along the path shown by the arrow. The record is read by a needle which follows the grooves.

Both devices produce an electrical signal, which is then converted into sound.

For each device, sketch the type of trace you would expect to see on a monitor.

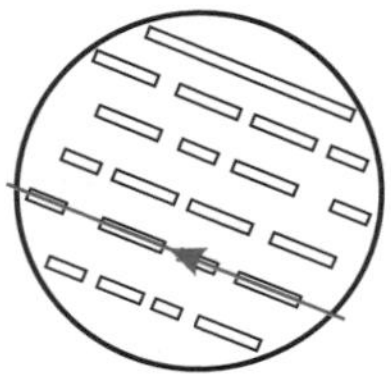

Compact disc

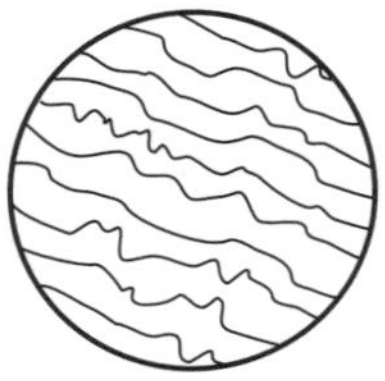

Old-fashioned record

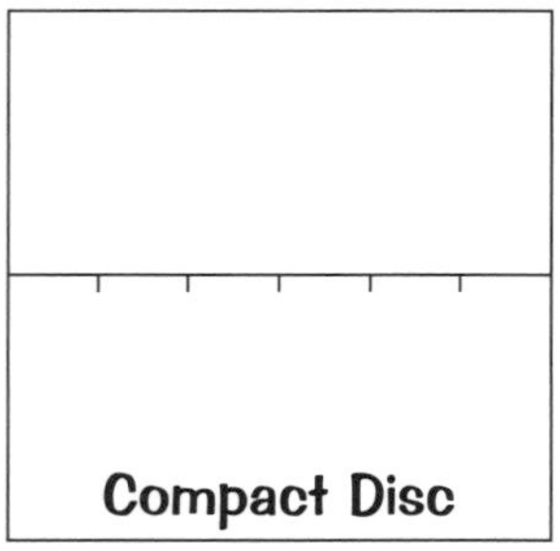

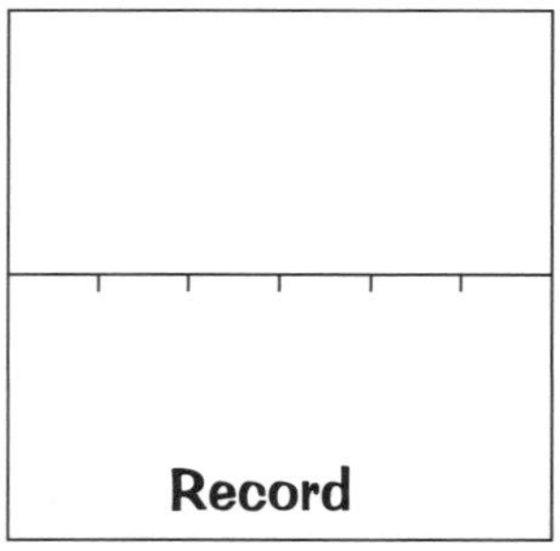

Seismic Waves

Q1 The diagram shows four **layers** of the Earth. Complete the table.

<u>Layer</u>	<u>Name</u>	<u>Solid or liquid</u>
A	core	
B		
C		
D		

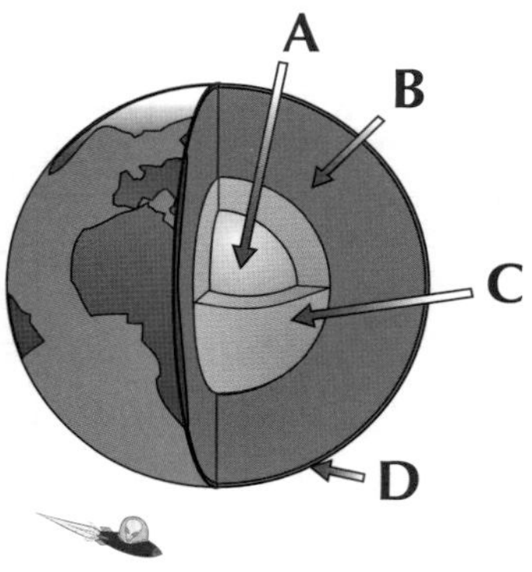

Q2 Earthquakes can produce both **S waves** and **P waves**.

a) Which of these two types are **longitudinal** waves? ....

b) Which waves travel **fastest**? ....

c) Which type of wave **cannot** travel through the **outer core** of the Earth? ....

d) Which type of wave can show a **sudden change of direction**? ....

Q3 Circle the letters of any **true** statements below.

a) **A** Both P and S waves can travel (in theory) from the North pole to the South pole.

B A longitudinal wave travels in the same direction as the force which causes it.

C Transverse waves travel at right angles to the force which causes them.

D P waves travel more slowly through the inner core. This suggests that it is made of solid material.

b) Rewrite any false statements to make them true.

....

....

Q4 Both P and S waves travel through the Earth in **curved** paths.

a) **Explain why** seismic waves curve as they travel through the Earth.

....

....

b) **i)** Which type of wave doesn't reach the area of the Earth that's opposite the site of the earthquake?

....

ii) What does this tell seismologists about the structure of the Earth?

....

Radioactivity

Q1 Fill in the blanks using the words below. Each word should be used only once.

radiation element protons neutrons nuclei radioactive

Isotopes are atoms which have the same number of .... but different numbers of .... Some isotopes are .... Their .... are unstable so they break down and spit out .... When this happens the nucleus often changes into a new ....

Q2 Carbon-14 is radioactive but carbon-12 is **not**.
Explain why, in terms of the difference between their **nuclei**.

....

....

Q3 Indicate whether these sentences are **true** or **false**.

		True	False
a)	The nucleus of an atom takes up almost no space compared to the whole atom.	☐	☐
b)	Most of an atom's mass is in the electrons.	☐	☐
c)	Radioactive decay speeds up at higher temperatures.	☐	☐

Q4 Complete the table below by choosing the correct word from each column.

Radiation Type	Ionising power weak/moderate/ strong	Charge positive/none/ negative	Relative mass no mass/ small/large	Penetrating power low/moderate/ high	Relative speed slow/fast/ very fast
alpha					
beta					
gamma					

Top Tips: If you've got a bunch of atoms with unstable nuclei, there's no way of telling which one is going to go first, or when it'll go. There's not even a number you can call to evict one.

Radioactivity

Q5 For each sentence, tick the correct box to show whether it is **true** or **false**.

		True	False
a)	All nuclear radiation is deflected by magnetic fields.	☐	☐
b)	Gamma radiation has no mass because it is an EM wave.	☐	☐
c)	Alpha is the slowest and most strongly ionising type of radiation.	☐	☐
d)	Beta particles are electrons, so they do not come from the nucleus.	☐	☐

Q6 Radiation from three sources — A, B and C — was directed through an **electric field** (between X and Y), towards target sheets of **paper**, **aluminium** and **lead**. Counters were used to detect where radiation passed through the target sheets.

Source A — the radiation was partially absorbed by the lead.
Source B — the radiation was deflected by the electric field and stopped by the paper.
Source C — the radiation was deflected by the electric field and stopped by the aluminium.

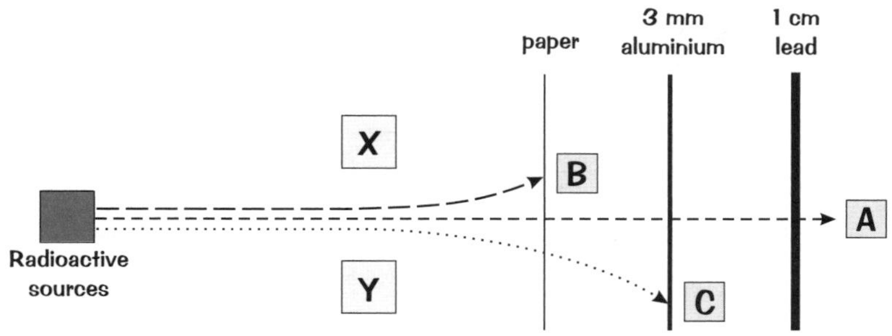

a) What type of radiation is emitted by:

source A? ...., source B? ...., source C? ....

b) Explain why radiation from source A is **not deflected** by the electric field.

....

....

c) What other type of **field** would deflect radiation from sources B and C? ....

Q7 Explain clearly why gamma rays are **less ionising** than alpha particles.

....

....

....

Background Radiation

Q1 Tick any of the following statements that are **true**.

- [ ] Radon gas is given off by rocks such as granite.
- [ ] Exposure to radon gas increases the risk of getting lung cancer.
- [ ] Scientists are sure that radon gas is only dangerous at high levels of concentration.
- [ ] If you live where there is a lot of radon gas, there is nothing you can do about it.
- [ ] The risk from radon gas is the same whether you smoke or not.

Q2 List **five** sources of background radiation.

....

....

Q3 Peter did an experiment to compare equal quantities of two radioactive materials. Here are his results and conclusion.

Material tested	Radiation measured (counts per second)
None	50
Material A	200
Material B	400

CONCLUSION
"Both materials are radioactive. Material B is twice as radioactive as Material A."

Is Peter's conclusion correct? Give a reason for your answer.

....

....

Q4 Radon gas building up in people's houses is a problem.

a) Explain why it's a problem.

....

b) Why is the level of radon gas in homes different in different parts of the country?

....

....

c) What can be done to reduce the build-up of radon gas in homes?

....

....

Half-Life

Q1 The graph shows how the count rate of a radioactive isotope decreases with time.

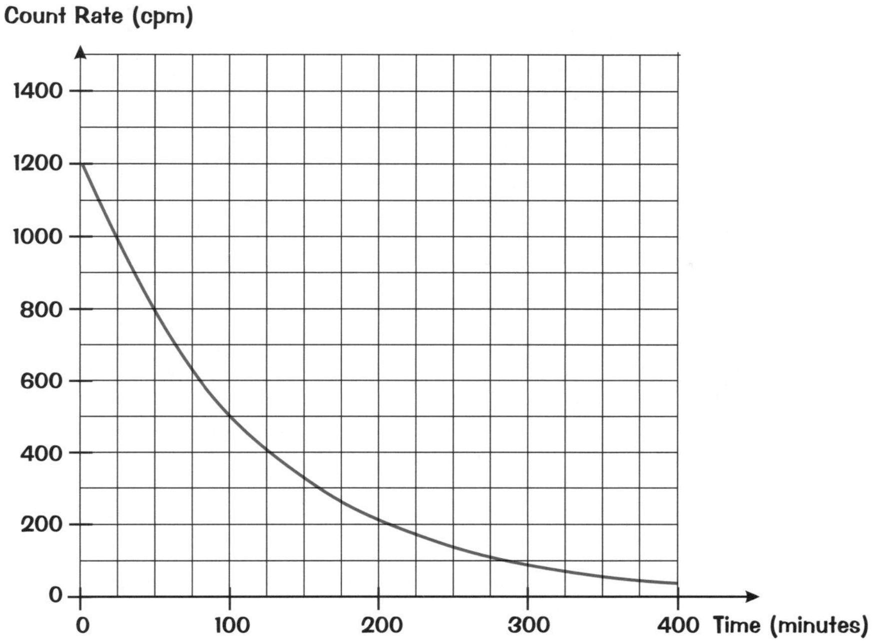

a) What is the half-life of this isotope? ....

b) What was the count rate after 3 half-lives? ....

c) What fraction of the original radioactive nuclei will still be unstable after 5 half-lives?

....

d) After how long was the count rate down to 100? ....

Q2 A radioactive isotope has a half-life of 40 seconds.

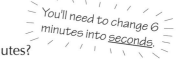

You'll need to change 6 minutes into seconds.

a) What fraction of the unstable nuclei will still be radioactive after 6 minutes?

....

....

b) **i)** If the initial count rate of the sample was 8000 counts per minute, what would be the approximate count rate after 6 minutes?

....

....

ii) After how many whole **minutes** would the count rate have fallen below 10 counts per minute?

....

....

Dangers from Nuclear Radiation

Q1 Two scientists are handling samples of radioactive material.

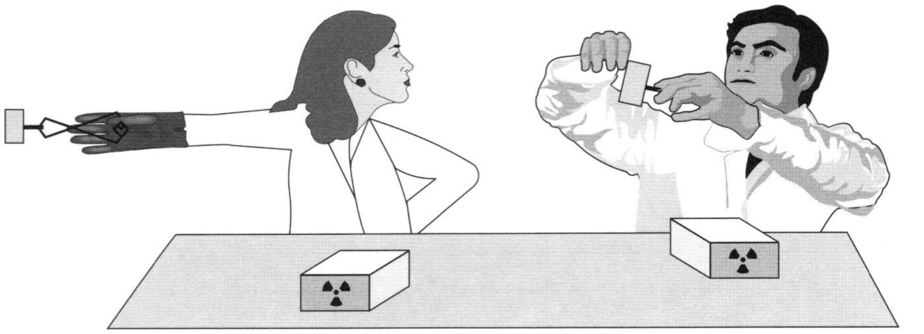

One of the scientists is taking **sensible safety precautions**, but the other is **not**.
Describe three things which the careless scientist is doing wrong.

1. ....

2. ....

3. ....

Q2 The three different types of radiation can **all** be dangerous.

a) Which **two** types of radiation can pass through the human body?
Circle the correct answers.

alpha   beta   gamma

b) **i)** Which type of radiation is usually most dangerous if it's **inhaled or swallowed**?

....

ii) What **effects** can this type of radiation have on the human body?

....

....

Q3 In industry, highly penetrating radiation sources sometimes need to be **moved** from place to place.

a) How can this be done without endangering the workers?

....

b) Gamma radiation can pass easily through the walls of buildings.
How can workers in the surrounding areas be protected from this hazard?

....

Top Tips: You should always handle radioactive sources really carefully. People who work with radioisotopes often wear **dosimeters** — badges which record their exposure. We're all exposed to a low level of **background radiation** every day, though — from rocks, etc. — and you can't do anything about that (unless you fancy wearing a lead-lined suit and breathing apparatus all day long).

Uses of Nuclear Radiation

Q1 The following sentences explain how a **smoke detector** works, but they are in the wrong order. Put them in order by labelling them 1 (first) to 6 (last).

- [ ] The circuit is broken so no current flows.
- [1] The radioactive source emits alpha particles.
- [ ] A current flows between the electrodes — the alarm stays off.
- [ ] The alarm sounds.
- [ ] The air between the electrodes is ionised by the alpha particles.
- [ ] A fire starts and smoke particles absorb the alpha radiation.

Q2 The diagram shows how **beta radiation** can be used in the control of paper thickness in a paper mill.

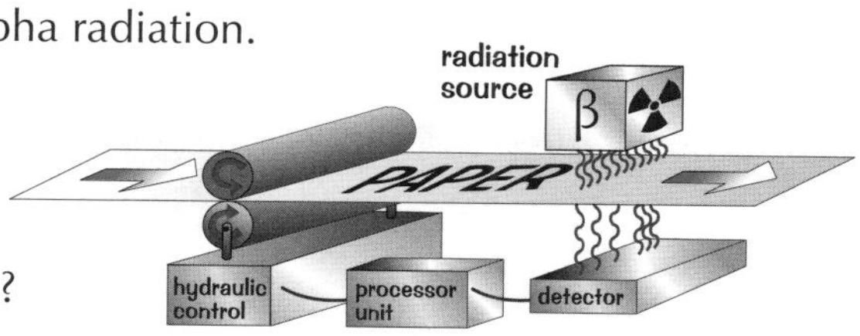

Why is beta radiation used rather than alpha or gamma?

....

....

Q3 Radiation can be used to **sterilise** surgical instruments.

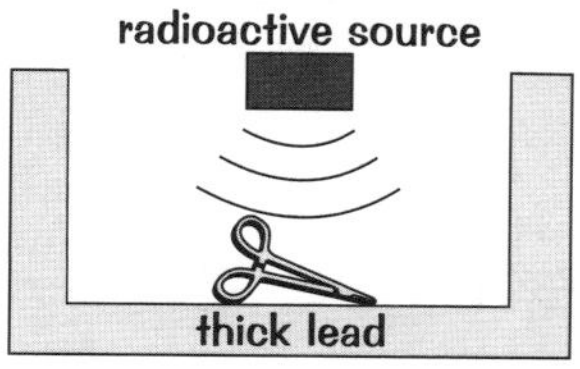

a) What kind of radioactive source is used, and why? In your answer, mention the **type** of radiation emitted (α, β and γ) and the **half-life** of the source.

....

....

....

b) What is the purpose of the **thick lead**?

....

c) Similar machines can be used to treat **fruit** before it is exported from South America to Europe, to stop it going bad on the long journey. How does irradiating the fruit help?

....

....

Q4 **Gamma radiation** can be used to test turbine blades in jet engines.

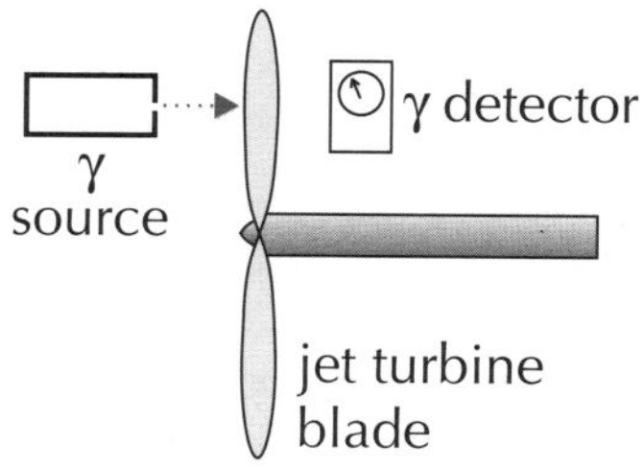

a) Explain how the test would detect a crack in the turbine blade.

....

....

b) How is this method preferable to hitting the blades with a hammer to test their strength?

....

Radioactive Dating

Q1 Carbon-14 makes up approximately 1 part in 10 000 000 of the carbon in living things.

a) What happens to the proportion of carbon-14 in a plant or animal when it dies?

....

b) The half-life of carbon-14 is 5730 years. Explain what this means in terms of the number of carbon-14 atoms in a sample.

....

Q2 A leather strap from an archaeological dig was found to have 1 part in 80 000 000 carbon-14.

a) Use the data given in Q1 to help you estimate the age of the strap.

....

....

b) Suggest two reasons why your answer to part a) might be inaccurate.

1. ....

2. ....

Q3 Some Egyptian leather sandals are known to be from 3700 BCE.

Approximately what fraction of the carbon in the sandals would you expect to be carbon-14?

....

Q4 A website is advertising "woolly mammoth tusks" for sale. An investigator buys one and carries out a radiocarbon test. The test shows that the tusk contains 1 part in 15 000 000 carbon-14.

Given that woolly mammoths are believed to have become extinct 10 000 years ago, is the tusk likely to be genuine? Explain your answer.

....

....

....

Q5 Uranium-238 decays with a half-life of 4.5 billion years into a stable form of lead.

A meteorite is found to contain some uranium-238 and some lead in the ratio of 1:1. If there was no lead in the meteorite when it was created, how old is the meteorite?

....

....

The Solar System

Q1 This diagram shows the objects in the Solar System. It **isn't to scale.**

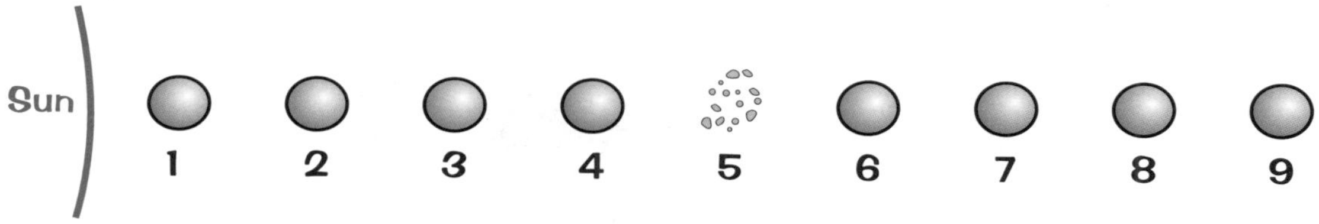

In the table below, write the correct number under each object's name to show its position in the Solar System.

Object	Mars	Jupiter	Asteroids	Venus	Saturn	Neptune	Earth	Mercury	Uranus
Number									

Q2 When Robert looks up into the night sky, he sees **stars** and **planets** (as long as it's a clear night).

Give three ways in which the planets that Robert sees are different from the stars he sees.

1. ....

2. ....

3. ....

Q3 The diagram shows the orbit of a **comet** around the Sun.

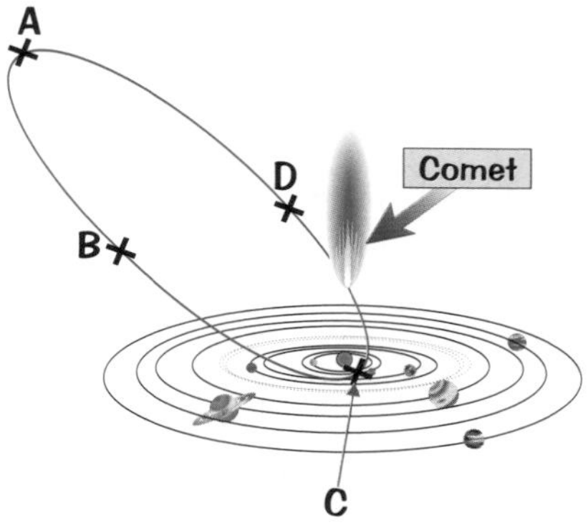

a) What is the name of the **shape** of the comet's orbit?

....

b) Write down the letters that show where the comet is travelling:

i) fastest: .... **ii)** slowest: ....

c) Explain your answers to part b).

....

....

d) **i)** What are comets made of? ....

ii) What causes the comet to have a 'tail'?

....

Q4 Some astronomers work on finding **Near-Earth Objects** (NEOs). Why is it important to track NEOs?

....

....

Magnetic Fields and Solar Flares

Q1 The diagram shows the Earth with an imaginary bar magnet inside it and its surrounding **magnetic field**.

a) Draw arrows on the dotted lines to show the **direction** of the Earth's magnetic field.

b) Complete the labels at the Earth's poles with the words "**north**" and "**south**".

c) Draw an **arrow on the compass** to show the direction it would point.

Q2 As well as light, the Sun also emits **cosmic radiation**. Cosmic radiation is mainly **charged particles** but it also contains two types of **rays**.

a) Name the two types of rays in cosmic radiation.

....

b) Give one effect of the charged particles hitting gas particles in the atmosphere.

....

c) Explain how the Earth's magnetic field helps to shield us from the charged particles in cosmic radiation.

....

Q3 From time to time, massive explosions called **solar flares** happen on the surface of the Sun.

Explain why solar flares can disturb the Earth's magnetic field.

....

Q4 This diagram shows the Earth's **magnetic field**.

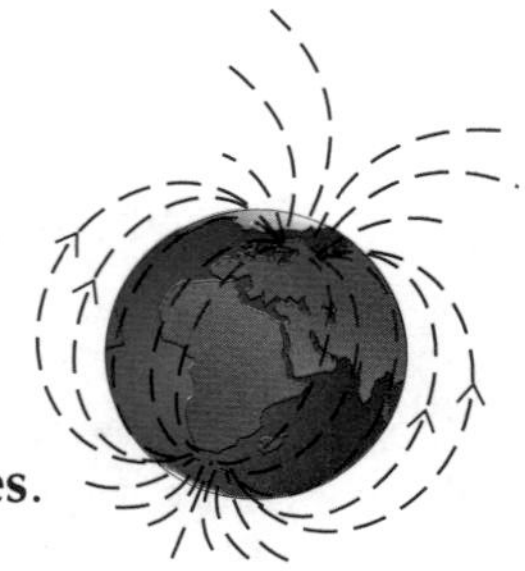

a) What do the **polar lights** (aurora borealis and aurora australis) look like?

....

b) Explain what **causes** the polar lights and why they appear near the **Earth's poles**. You can use the diagram on the right to help you.

....

....

Beyond the Solar System

Q1 One of the following statements is **not true**. Circle the letter next to the false statement.

A Most galaxies are made up of billions of stars.

B The distance between galaxies can be millions of times the distance between stars.

C Gravity is the force which keeps stars apart.

D Galaxies rotate in space.

E Planets are formed from the same clouds of gas and dust as stars.

Q2 The **light year** is a unit of length.

a) Write down the definition of a light year.

b) Calculate the length **in km** of one **light year**, given that:

1 day = 24 hours

1 year = 365.25 days

Speed of light = 3×10^8 m/s.

Watch out for units — the answer has to be in km, not m.

c) The Milky Way is about 100 000 light years in diameter. The Solar System is about halfway along one of the Galaxy's spiral arms. Use your answer to part b) to calculate how far we are from the centre of the Galaxy, in **km**. Give your answer in standard form, to 3 significant figures.

Q3 **Black holes** are the last stages in the lives of big stars.

a) Explain in terms of gravity why black holes are black.

b) How do scientists detect black holes?

The Life Cycle of Stars

Q1 A star in its **stable** phase **doesn't get bigger or smaller**, even though there are forces tending to make it expand and forces trying to make it contract.

a) What causes the outward pressure on the star?

....

b) What is the force pulling the star inwards? ....

c) Why doesn't the star expand or contract? ....

....

d) What is the name given to a star in its stable phase? ....

Q2 Stars are formed from clouds of dust and gas.

a) **Why** does the material come together?

....

b) Where does most of the **heat and light energy** emitted by a star come from?

....

Marilyn was nearing the end of her stable phase

Q3 Old stars eventually turn into **red giants**.

a) What causes a star to become a red giant? ....

....

b) Why is a red giant red? ....

....

Q4 Complete the passage below to describe what eventually happens to red giants.

A small star will cool and contract into a ...., before fading completely into a .... A bigger star will explode as a ...., leaving a very dense core called a .... The biggest stars form .... instead.

Due to printing restrictions, red giants are currently unavailable.

Q5 Explain what happens in a **big star** during its **red giant** phase.

....

....

The Origins of the Universe

Q1 The **Big Bang theory** is the accepted scientific explanation for the origin of the Universe.

a) Complete this passage using the words supplied below.

expansion   matter   energy   expand   age   explosion

Many scientists believe that the Universe started with all the .... and .... in one small space. There was a huge .... and the Universe started to .... Scientists can estimate the .... of the Universe using the current rate of ....

b) Why are estimates of the age of the Universe quite **unreliable**?

....

Q2 What **evidence** is there to support the idea that the Universe began with a 'Big Bang'? Include a brief explanation of **red-shift** and **cosmic background radiation** in your answer.

....

....

....

....

Q3 The **eventual fate** of the Universe is not yet known for certain.

a) Give **two factors** that the fate of the Universe depends upon.

....

b) What is **dark matter** and how can scientists detect it?

....

....

Q4 **Visible matter** provides about 4% of the gravity needed to halt the Universe's expansion.

a) If the dark matter in the universe has **30 times the mass** of the visible matter, how will the Universe end?

....

b) If the dark matter has only **twice** the mass of the visible matter, what will happen?

....

Exploring the Solar System

Q1 Scientists estimate that a round trip to **Mars** would take astronauts up to **2 years** to complete. Identify four problems associated with such a journey.

1. ....

2. ....

3. ....

4. ....

Q2 Scientists have already landed **unmanned probes** on Mars.

a) Outline two advantages of using unmanned probes.

....

....

....

b) Describe one disadvantage of using unmanned probes.

....

....

c) Probes designed to land safely on the surface may carry **exploration rovers** which can explore their surroundings and collect data.

i) Suggest what kinds of investigation could be carried out by an exploration rover.

....

....

....

ii) Several probes intended to land on Mars have failed — they've been damaged too badly to work. Suggest why it is so difficult to land a probe safely.

....

....

....

Looking into Space

Q1 Patrick lives in central **London** and loves to look at the stars using a telescope in his back garden. Would Patrick be able to see stars **more** or **less clearly** if he used his telescope in the countryside? Explain your answer.

....

....

....

....

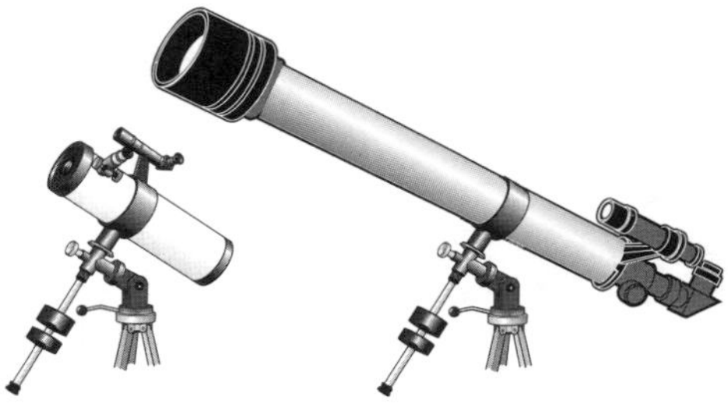

Q2 Astronomers can use a number of strategies to improve the quality of the images they get of space from Earth-based telescopes.

a) How can they get good images of **faint**, **distant** objects using optical telescopes?

....

....

....

b) How can they improve an optical telescope's **resolution** (ability to see detail)?

....

....

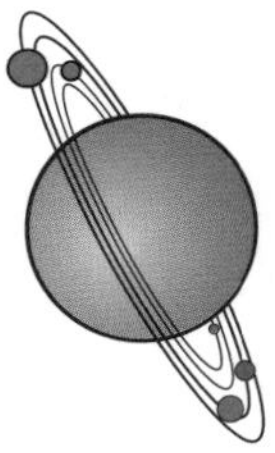

Q3 The **Hubble Space Telescope** can produce images which are much better than those from any Earth-based optical telescopes of a similar size.

a) Explain why the pictures from the Hubble Telescope are clearer and brighter.

....

....

b) List **three** possible **disadvantages** of using space telescopes.

1. ....

2. ....

3. ....

Looking into Space

Q4 Astronomers use various telescopes designed to collect different types of electromagnetic waves. Why do they not just use **optical telescopes** situated on Earth or in space?

....

....

....

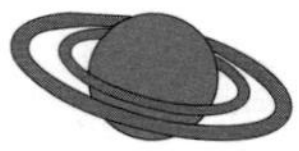

Q5 **Radio telescopes** need to be very large, or else the images are 'fuzzy' and lack detail.

a) Why is this?

....

....

....

b) To produce images with a similar degree of detail, which would need to be **larger** — an infrared telescope or an ultraviolet telescope? Circle the correct answer.

infrared ultraviolet

Q6 Astronomers can't use X-ray telescopes on Earth.

Explain why this is.

....

....

....

Top Tips: With telescopes, the rule seems to be 'big is beautiful'. And it's best to think up a good name to make sure everyone knows your telescope's the biggest. There's one in Chile called the Very Large Telescope. Imaginative. There were plans to build a really big new optical telescope — 100 m across — and call it the Overwhelmingly Large Telescope. Something to prove, hmm?

Velocity and Acceleration

Q1 A pulse of laser light takes 1.3 seconds to travel from the Moon to the Earth. The speed of light is approximately 3×10^8 m/s.

You'll need to rearrange the speed formula.

How far away is the Moon from the Earth? Give your answer in km.

Q2 An egg is dropped from the top of the Eiffel tower. It hits the ground after 8 seconds, at a speed of 80 m/s.

a) Calculate the egg's acceleration.

b) How long did it take for the egg to reach a velocity of 40 m/s?

Q3 Ealing is about 12 km west of Marble Arch. It takes a tube train 20 minutes to get to Marble Arch from Ealing.

Only **one** of the following statements is true. Circle the appropriate letter.

A The average speed of the train is 60 m/s.

B The average velocity of the train is 10 m/s.

C The average velocity of the train is 60 m/s due east.

D The average speed of the train is 10 m/s.

E The average velocity of the train is 10 m/s due west.

Q4 Paolo and some friends want to order a takeaway. Paolo writes down what they know about the two nearest takeaways:

Ludo's Pizza

- Time taken to cook the food is 1/4 hour
- Distance to the house is 6.5 km
- Deliver on scooters with average speed of 30 km/h

Moonlight Indian Takeaway

- Time taken to cook the food is 1/2 hour
- Distance to the house is 4 km
- Delivery van has average speed of 40 km/h

Remember to add on the time taken to cook the food.

Which takeaway should they order from to get their food the **quickest**?

Q5 A car accelerates at 2 m/s^2. After 4 seconds it reaches a speed of 24 m/s.

How fast was it going before it started to accelerate?

D-T and V-T Graphs

Q1 Steve walked to football training only to find that he'd left his boots at home. He turned round and walked back home, where he spent 30 seconds looking for them. To make it to training on time he had to run back at twice his walking speed.

Below is an incomplete **distance-time graph** for Steve's journey.

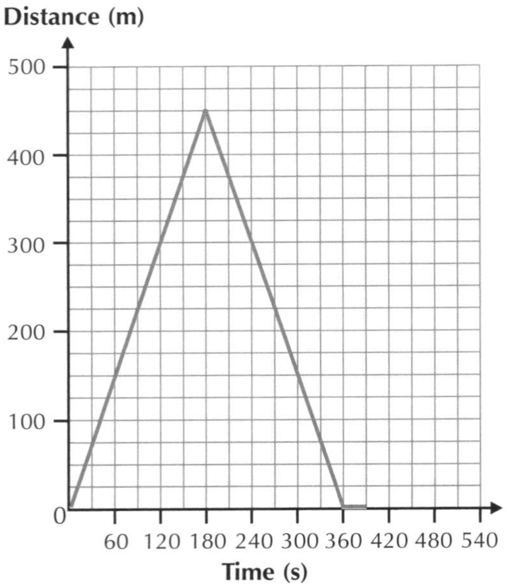

a) How long did it take Steve to walk to training?

....

b) Calculate Steve's speed (in m/s) as he walked to training.

....

....

c) Complete the graph to show Steve's run back from his house to training (with his boots).

Q2 The speed limit for cars on motorways is 70 mph (31 m/s). A motorist was stopped for speeding as she joined the motorway from a service station.

The distance-time graph on the right shows the car's acceleration. The motorist denied speeding. Was she telling the truth?

....

....

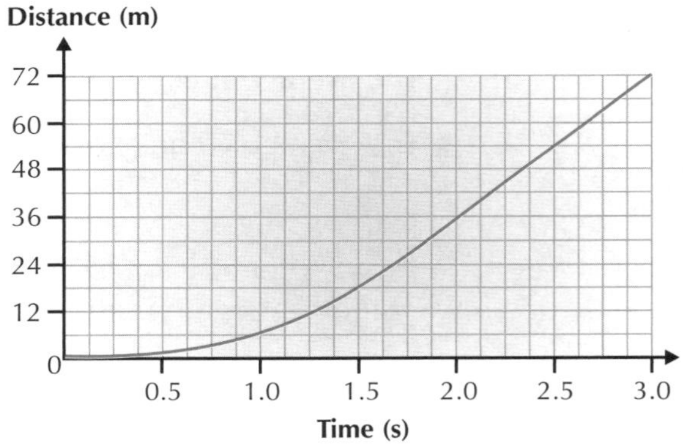

Q3 A motorist saw a puppy asleep on the road 25 m in front of him. It took him 0.75 seconds to react and slam on the brakes. The velocity-time graph below shows the car's deceleration.

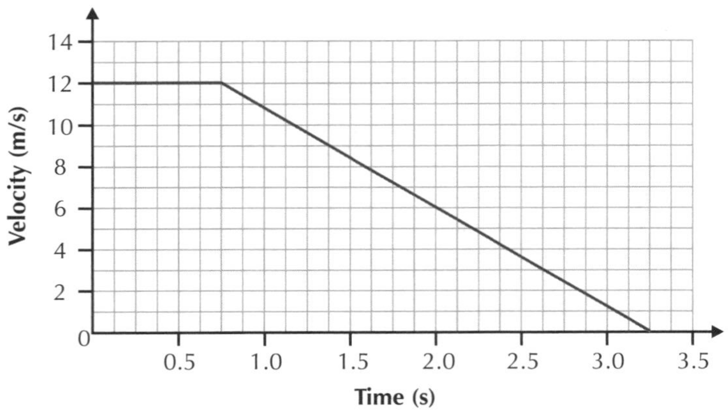

It helps to split the graph up into two smaller shapes.

Use the graph to work out whether the motorist stopped before hitting the puppy.

....

....

....

Mass, Weight and Gravity

Q1 Which is the correct explanation for why the Moon orbits the Earth? Tick the appropriate box.

- ☐ There is an attractive force between the weights of the Earth and Moon.
- ☐ They attract each other as they have masses caused by them having weight.
- ☐ The weight of the Moon acts downwards.
- ☐ There is an attractive force between the masses of the Earth and Moon.
- ☐ The mass of the Moon acts downwards.

Q2 Two mad scientists are planning a trip to Mars.

a) Professor White tells Professor Brown —

"We won't need so much fuel for the return trip — the rocket will have less mass on Mars."

Is Professor White's reasoning correct? Explain your answer. (Ignore the fuel burned reaching Mars).

....

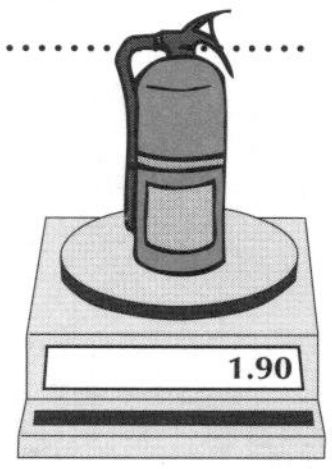

b) Professor Brown wants to investigate gravity on Mars. He takes to Mars a small fire extinguisher which weighs 50 N on Earth. He also takes his bathroom scales.

On Mars, Professor Brown weighs the fire extinguisher.
The scales read **1.9 kg**.
Calculate the **acceleration due to gravity** on Mars.

Find the mass of the fire extinguisher first.

....

....

....

Q3 A space probe lands on the icy surface of **Europa**, a moon of Jupiter. It weighs a set of **known masses**, but the readings are not very accurate. **Plot a graph** on the axes using the information from the table, and use it to **estimate** the **strength of Europa's gravity**.

Mass	Weight
0.1 kg	0.15 N
0.2 kg	0.30 N
0.3 kg	0.36 N
0.4 kg	0.55 N
0.5 kg	0.68 N

Graph of Weight Against Mass

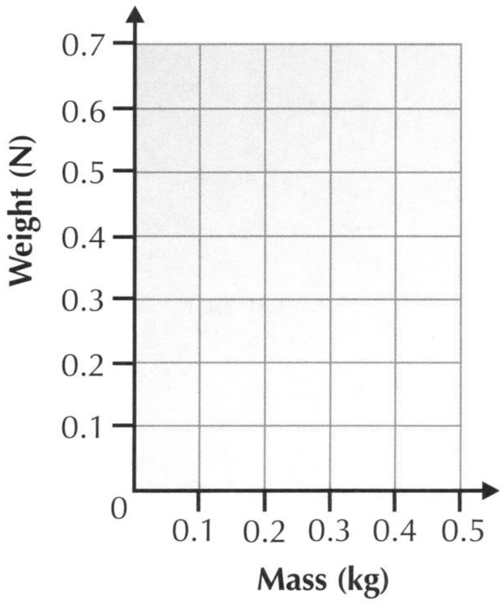

....

....

....

....

The Three Laws of Motion

Q1 Use the words below to fill in the blanks.

proportional	force	reaction	stationary	accelerates	opposite
	constant	resultant	inversely	balanced	

Newton's 1st law: If the forces on an object are .... , it's either .... or moving at .... speed.

Newton's 2nd law: If an object has a .... force acting on it, it .... in the direction of the ....
The acceleration is .... to the force and .... to the mass.

Newton's 3rd law: For every action there is an equal and ....

Q2 Otto is driving the school bus at a **steady speed** along a level road.
Tick the boxes next to any of the following statements which are **true**.

- ☐ The driving force of the engine is bigger than the friction and air resistance combined.
- ☐ The driving force of the engine is equal to the friction and air resistance combined.
- ☐ There are no forces acting on the bus.
- ☐ No force is required to keep the bus moving.

Q3 State whether the **forces** acting on these objects are **balanced** or **unbalanced**. Explain your answers.

a) A **cricket ball** slowing down as it rolls along the outfield.

....

b) A **car** going round a roundabout at a steady 30 mph.

....

c) A **vase** knocked off a window ledge.

....

d) A **satellite** orbiting over a fixed point on the Earth's surface.

....

e) A **bag of rubbish** which was ejected from a spacecraft in empty space.

....

The Three Laws of Motion

Q4 The table below shows the **masses** and **maximum accelerations** of four different antique cars.

Car	Mass (kg)	Maximum acceleration (m/s²)
Disraeli 9000	800	5
Palmerston 6i	1560	0.7
Heath TT	950	3
Asquith 380	790	2

Write down the names of the four cars in order of increasing driving force.

....

Q5 Jo and Brian have fitted both their scooters with the same engine. When he's sat on it, Brian's scooter has a mass of 110 kg and an acceleration of 2.80 m/s². Jo only manages an acceleration of 1.71 m/s² on her scooter.

a) What **force** can the engine exert?

....

b) Calculate the total mass of Jo and her scooter.

....

Q6 A spacecraft launches a probe at a constant speed. A day later, the probe returns at the same speed.

Did the probe have to burn any fuel? Explain your answer.

....

....

Q7 Maisie drags a **1 kg** mass along a table with a newton-meter so that it accelerates at **0.25 m/s²**. The newton-meter reads **0.4 N**. Calculate the force of friction between the mass and the table.

....

....

Q8 Which of the following statements correctly explains what happens when you walk? Circle the appropriate letter.

A Your feet push the ground backwards, so the ground pushes you forwards.

B The force in your muscles overcomes the friction between your feet and the ground.

C The ground's reaction can't push you backwards because of friction.

D Your feet push forwards, and the ground's reaction is upwards.

Friction Forces and Terminal Speed

Q1 Choose from the words supplied to fill in the blanks in the paragraph below about a skydiver.

decelerates decrease less balances increase constant greater accelerates

When a skydiver jumps out of a plane, his weight is .... than his air resistance, so he .... downwards. This causes his air resistance to .... until it .... his weight. At this point, his velocity is .... When his parachute opens, his air resistance is .... than his weight, so he .... This causes his air resistance to .... until it .... his weight. Then his velocity is .... once again.

Q2 Which of the following will **reduce** the drag force on an aeroplane? Tick all appropriate boxes.

- ☐ flying higher (where the air is thinner)
- ☐ carrying less cargo
- ☐ flying more slowly
- ☐ making the plane more streamlined

Q3 A scientist plans to investigate gravity by dropping a hammer and a feather from a tall building. Two onlookers predict what will happen. Say whether each is right or wrong, and explain why.

Paola: "They will land at the same time — gravity is the same for both."

Guiseppe: "The feather will reach its terminal velocity before the hammer."

a) Paola is **right** / **wrong** because ....

....

b) Guiseppe is **right** / **wrong** because ....

....

Q4 Mavis is investigating **drag** by dropping balls into a measuring cylinder full of oil and timing how long they take to reach the bottom. She does the experiment with a **golf ball**, a **glass marble** and a **ball bearing**.

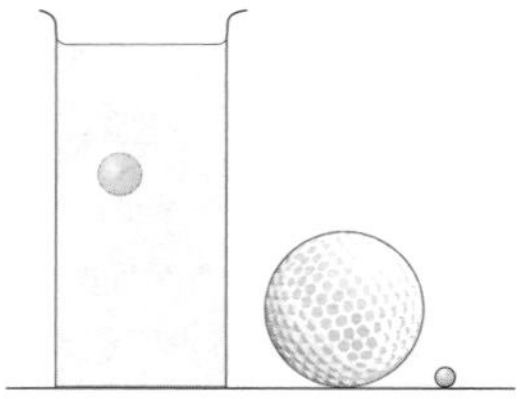

From this experiment, can Mavis draw any conclusions about the effect of size on drag? Explain your answer.

....

....

Top Tips: When an object moves through the air at high speed, the air resistance is proportional to the object's **velocity squared**. That's why, for skydivers, air resistance soon balances their weight and they reach terminal velocity. It's also why **driving** very fast is very **inefficient**.

Stopping Distances

Q1 **Stopping distance** and **braking distance** are not the same thing.

a) What is meant by 'braking distance'?

....

b) Use the words in the box to complete the following word equations.

braking	speed	reaction time	thinking

i) Thinking distance = ... × ....

ii) Stopping distance = ... distance + ... distance.

Q2 Will the following factors affect **thinking** distance, **braking** distance or **both**? Write them in the relevant columns of the table.

tiredness   road surface   weather   speed   alcohol   tyres   brakes   load

Thinking Distance	Braking Distance

Q3 A car joins a motorway and changes speed from 30 mph to 60 mph. Which one of the following statements is **true**? Tick the appropriate box.

- ☐ The total stopping distance will double.
- ☐ The braking distance will double.
- ☐ Thinking distance will double and braking distance will more than double.
- ☐ Both thinking and braking distance will more than double.

Q4 A car has just driven through a deep puddle, making the brakes wet. Explain why this will increase the stopping distance of the car.

....

....

Momentum and Collisions

Q1 Place the following four trucks in order of increasing momentum.

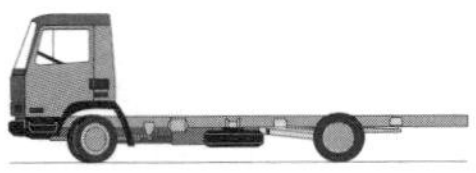

Truck A
speed = 30 m/s
mass = 3000 kg

Truck B
speed = 10 m/s
mass = 4500 kg

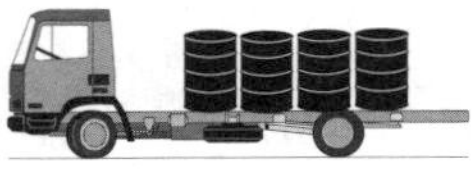

Truck C
speed = 20 m/s
mass = 4000 kg

Truck D
speed = 15 m/s
mass = 3500 kg

(lowest momentum) .... , ... , ... , ... (highest momentum)

Q2 A skateboarder with a mass of 60 kg is moving at 5 m/s. He skates past his bag, picks it up from the floor and slows down to 4.8 m/s. Assuming no friction, find the mass of the skater's bag.

You might find it helpful to draw a diagram showing the masses and velocities involved.

Q3 A rocket is stationary in empty space. It is then propelled forwards by quickly releasing exhaust gases in the opposite direction. Indicate which of the following statements are **true**.

- ☐ The velocity of the exhaust gas is equal and opposite to the rocket's velocity.
- ☐ The momentum of the exhaust gas is equal and opposite to the rocket's momentum.
- ☐ The velocity of the exhaust gas is greater than the rocket's velocity.
- ☐ The momentum of the exhaust gas is greater than the rocket's momentum.

Q4 A 750 kg car is travelling at 30 m/s along the motorway. It crashes into the barrier of the central reservation and is stopped in a period of 1.2 seconds.

a) Find the size of the **average force** acting on the car to stop it.

b) Explain in terms of the forces acting why the occupants of the car are likely to be less severely injured if they are wearing seat belts made of slightly **stretchy** material.

Car Safety

Q1 A motorist drives along a level road and brakes to avoid hitting a cat.

a) What type of **energy** does the moving car have?

....

b) Explain how energy is **conserved** as the brakes slow down the car.

....

....

Q2 Modern cars are fitted with many **safety features**.

a) Why are car safety features often designed to slow the car and passengers down over a **long time**?

....

....

b) How do the following features achieve this?

i) Crumple zones ....

ii) Air bags ....

Q3 Use the words supplied to fill in the blanks in the passage below.

crashes skidding safety steering lock power interact control

Many modern cars have active .... features. These .... with the way the car is driven to help avoid ....

These features include .... assisted steering and traction ....

ABS brakes stop the car .... by making sure the wheels don't .... and so the driver can always control the .... of the car.

Q4 **Roads** themselves can be designed to be safer. Explain how **crash barriers** keep passengers safer in a collision.

....

....

Work and Potential Energy

Q1 Circle the correct words to make the following sentences true.

a) Work involves the transfer of **force** / **heat** / **energy**.

b) To do work **a force** / **an acceleration** acts over a **distance** / **time**.

c) Work is measured in **watts** / **joules**.

Q2 Indicate whether the following statements are **true** or **false**.

	True	False
a) Work is done when a toy car is pushed along the ground.	☐	☐
b) No work is done if a force is applied to an object which does not move.	☐	☐
c) Gravity does work on an apple that is not moving.	☐	☐
d) Gravity does work on an apple that falls out of a tree.	☐	☐

Q3 An elephant exerts a constant force of **1200 N** to push a donkey along a track at a steady 1 m/s.

a) Calculate the work done by the elephant if the donkey moves **8 m**.

....

b) From where does the elephant get the energy to do this work? ....

c) Into what form(s) is this energy transferred when work is done on the donkey?

....

Q4 Ben's mass is 60 kg. He climbs a ladder. The rungs of the ladder are 20 cm apart.

a) What force(s) is Ben doing work **against** as he climbs?

....

b) As he climbs, what happens to the **energy** supplied by Ben's muscles?

....

....

c) How much work does Ben do when he climbs **10 rungs**? (Ignore any 'wasted' energy.) Assume that g = 10 N/kg.

....

....

d) How many rungs of the ladder must Ben climb before he has done **15 kJ** of work? (Ignore any 'wasted' energy.) Assume that g = 10 N/kg.

....

....

Kinetic Energy

Q1 Find the **kinetic energy** of a 200 kg tiger running at a speed of 9 m/s.

....

....

Q2 A golf ball is hit and given 9 J of kinetic energy.
The ball's velocity is 20 m/s. What is its **mass?**

....

....

Q3 A 4 g bullet is fired from a rifle with a kinetic energy of 2 kJ.
What is the **speed** of the bullet when it leaves the rifle?

....

....

Q4 The **braking distance** for a car travelling at **30 mph** is approximately **14 m.**
At **50 mph** the braking distance is about **38 m.**

Explain, in terms of kinetic energy, why the braking distance more than doubles when the car's speed is less than doubled.

....

....

Q5 A skier with a mass of 70 kg rides a chairlift up a ski slope to a height of 20 m.
She then skis back down to the bottom of the chairlift.

a) Calculate the **work done** against gravity by the chairlift in carrying the skier up the slope. (Assume that g = 10 N/kg.)

....

....

b) Find the skier's **maximum speed** when she reaches the bottom of the chairlift.

....

....

Top Tips: Kinetic energy's all about moving — the bigger something's mass and the faster it's going, the larger the kinetic energy. Get comfy working with the formulas as they crop up everywhere, especially in energy conservation questions. It's pretty simple stuff — so get learning.

Roller Coasters

Q1 A roller coaster carriage and passengers are stationary at the top of a ride. At this point they have a gravitational potential energy of **300 kJ**.

a) Draw lines to connect each stage of the roller coaster with the correct energy statement.

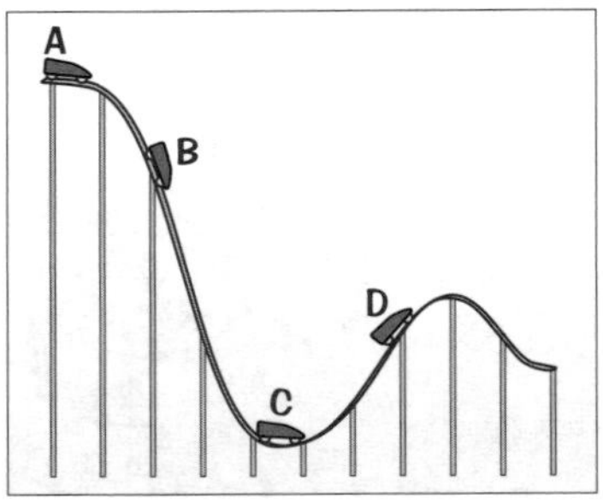

A	minimum P.E., maximum K.E.
B	K.E. is being converted to P.E.
C	P.E. is being converted to K.E.
D	maximum P.E.

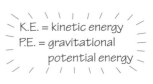

K.E. = kinetic energy
P.E. = gravitational potential energy

b) **i)** When the carriage has dropped to half its original height, what is the maximum **kinetic energy** it could have?

....

ii) Explain why in real life the kinetic energy is **less** than this.

....

c) Chris thinks that a **heavier** roller coaster carriage will go **faster** downhill than a lighter one. Is he right? Give a reason for your answer.

....

Q2 On the planet Greldar, a full roller coaster carriage has a mass of **1500 kg**.

a) If **g = 15 N/kg**, calculate the **weight** of a full carriage.

....

b) At the start of the ride, the roller coaster rises up to its highest point of **25 m**.

i) What is its gain in gravitational **potential energy**?

....

ii) How much **work** does the motor need to do to get the roller coaster to the top of the ride?

....

c) The first drop of the roller coaster takes the carriage from a height of 25 m to a height of 7 m.

i) What is its change in gravitational **potential energy**?

....

ii) Assuming no friction, how fast is the carriage going at the bottom of the dip?

....

....

Power

Q1 Tom likes to build model boats. His favourite boat is the Carter, which has a motor power of **150 W**.

a) How much **energy** does the Carter's motor transfer in **10 minutes**?

....

b) If the petrol for the boat's motor contains **30 kJ/ml**, how much is used up in **10 minutes**?

....

c) Tom decides to get a model speed boat which transfers **120 kJ** in the same 10 minute journey. What is the **power** of the engine?

....

Q2 Josie runs home after school so she can watch her favourite TV programme. She has a mass of **60 kg** and her school bag weighs **5 kg**.

a) At the start of her run, she accelerates from **0** to **8 m/s** in **6 seconds** whilst carrying her bag. Calculate her power output for this part of her run.

....

b) Josie gets to her house, puts **down** her school bag, and then runs up the stairs to her room. It takes her **4 seconds** to get to the top of the stairs where she is **5 m** above ground level. How much power does she generate getting up the stairs?

....

Q3 Andy loves running and wants to improve his starts in sprint races. He uses a timing gate to measure his maximum speed and how long the start takes him. He has a mass of **70 kg**.

Sprint number	Time taken (s)	Maximum speed (m/s)
1	3.2	8.0
2	3.1	8.2
3	3.3	7.9
4	4.6 *	7.2
5	3.2	7.9

* He slips because his shoes don't grip properly.

a) The information from one of the sprints should be ignored. Which one?

....

b) What is Andy's average **power** over the reliable starts?

....

....

....

....

Fuels for Cars

Q1 Petrol is made from oil, which is a **fossil fuel**.

a) Are fossil fuels **renewable** or **non-renewable**? ....

b) Give **two** environmental problems that burning fossil fuels in cars can cause.

1. ....

2. ....

c) Give an example of an 'alternative fuel' to petrol and diesel. ....

Q2 Trevor's car has two engines, a normal **petrol engine** and an **electric motor**. He uses the electric motor for short journeys but uses the petrol engine for longer drives.

a) How does using the electric motor cause less damage to the **environment**?

....

b) Explain why Trevor has to use the petrol engine for **longer** journeys.

....

c) The electric motor is powered by batteries that need to be frequently charged from a mains supply. If Trevor always used the electric motor, would his driving have any impact on the environment? Explain your answer.

....

....

Q3 A car's fuel consumption is **3.4 l/100 km**. How much fuel is used in a **250 km** journey? Tick the correct box.

☐ 3.4 l   ☐ 8.5 l   ☐ 6.8 l   ☐ 10.0 l

Q4 The fuel consumption of a car can **vary**.

a) State whether the following will **increase** or **decrease** the fuel consumption of a moving car, and explain why.

i) Roof racks ....

....

ii) Open windows ....

....

b) How does fuel consumption vary with the **speed** of a car?

....

Static Electricity

Q1 Fill in the gaps in these sentences with the words below.

electrons	positive	static	friction	insulating	negative

.... electricity can build up when two .... materials are rubbed together. The .... moves .... from one material onto the other. This leaves a .... charge on one of the materials and a .... charge on the other.

Q2 **Circle** the pairs of charges that would attract each other and **underline** those that would repel.

positive and positive   positive and negative   negative and positive   negative and negative

Q3 A **Van de Graaff generator** is a machine which is used to generate static electricity. One type of Van de Graaff generator works like this:

1. The bottom comb is positively charged and attracts electrons away from the rubber belt.
2. The rubber belt loses electrons and becomes positively charged.
3. As the positive charge on the belt passes the top comb, electrons are attracted from the metal dome onto the belt.
4. The dome loses electrons and builds up a positive charge.

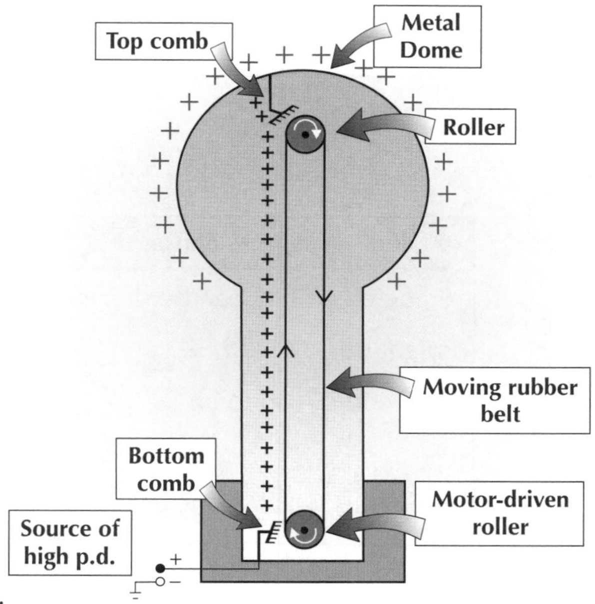

a) Why is the belt made of rubber?

....

b) The top comb needs to be a **conductor**. Explain why.

....

....

c) Nadia is doing an experiment with a Van de Graaff generator. Her teacher tells her that if she touches the generator she will become charged. When Nadia touches the generator her hair starts to stand on end.

Use your knowledge of electrostatic charges to **explain why** Nadia's hair stands on end.

....

....

Static Electricity

Q4 Three friends are talking about static electricity on their clothes.

Why do some of my clothes get charged up during the day?
Do cotton clothes get charged as much as nylon clothes?
Why do I hear a crackling sound when I take off my shirt?
Lisa
Tim
Sara

Answer their questions in the spaces below.

Lisa: ....

....

Sara: ....

....

Tim: ....

....

Q5 Use the words below to fill in the gaps.

fuel	grain chutes	paper rollers	sparks	explosion	earthed

Static electricity can be dangerous when refuelling cars. If too much static builds up, there might be .... which can set fire to the .... This could lead to an .... To prevent this happening, the nozzle is .... so the charge is conducted away. There are similar safety problems with .... and ....

Q6 Match up these phrases to describe what happens in a **thunderstorm**. Write out your complete sentences below in the correct order.

If the voltage gets big enough...

... the voltage gets higher and higher.

The bottoms of the clouds become negatively charged...

... and electrons move between them.

As the charge increases...

... there is a huge spark (a flash of lightning).

Raindrops and ice bump together...

... because they gain extra electrons.

1. ....
2. ....
3. ....
4. ....

Uses of Static Electricity

Q1 Choose from the words below to fill in the gaps.
You may need to use some words more than once.

defibrillator	earthed	shock	precipitator	sparks	paddles	insulated

The beating of your heart is controlled by tiny little electrical pulses, so an electric .... to a stopped heart can make it start beating again. This is done with a machine called a .... The machine uses two .... connected to a power supply.
It's important that only the patient receives a ...., so the operator holds .... handles.

Q2 A **smoke precipitator** stops smoke particles from escaping up a chimney.

Explain why:

a) the smoke is made to pass through a wire grid with a high negative charge.

....

b) the metal collection plates are also charged up.

....

c) the smoke particles stick to the metal plates.

....

Q3 In a **photocopier**, the image plate is **positively** charged.

a) Why do some parts of the image plate lose their charge?

....

....

b) Explain why the black powder sticks to the image plate.

....

c) Describe what would happen if the paper wasn't charged.

....

Top Tips: Static electricity's responsible for many of life's little annoyances — like bad hair days and those little shocks you get from touching car doors. Still, it has its uses too.

Circuits — The Basics

Q1 Use the words in the box to fill in the gaps. Use each word once only.

more
voltage
resistance
less
current
force

a) The flow of electrons round a circuit is called the ....

b) .... is the .... that pushes the current round the circuit.

c) If you increase the voltage, ... current will flow.

d) If you increase the ...., ... current will flow.

Q2 Match up these items from a standard test circuit with the **correct description** and **symbol**.

ITEM	DESCRIPTION
Cell	The item you're testing.
Variable Resistor	Provides the voltage.
Component	Measures the voltage.
Voltmeter	Used to alter the current.

SYMBOL

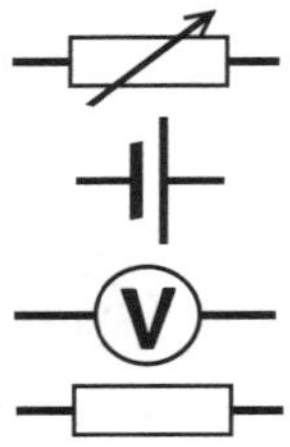

Q3 Write down:

a) the **unit** of:

i) current .... **ii)** voltage .... **iii)** resistance ....

b) two ways of **decreasing** the current in a standard test circuit:

1. ....

2. ....

Q4 Indicate whether these statements are **true** or **false**.
Write out a **correct version** of each false statement.

	True	False
a) Conventional current flows from positive to negative.	☐	☐
b) An ammeter should be connected in parallel with a component.	☐	☐
c) Items that are in series can be in any order.	☐	☐
d) A voltmeter should be connected in series with a component.	☐	☐

....

....

....

....

Resistance and Devices

Q1 Write out the names of the **numbered circuit devices** in the spaces below.

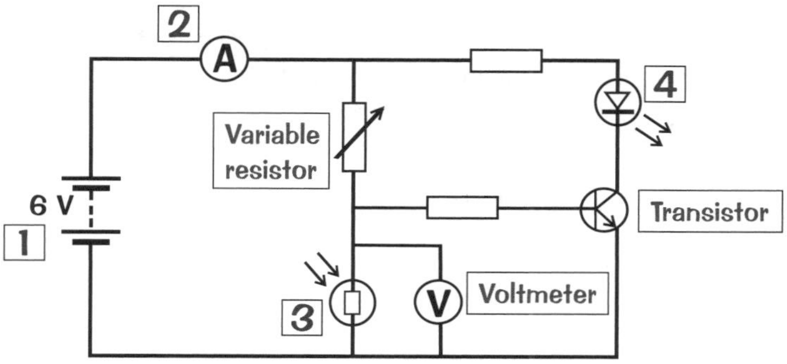

1. ....
2. ....
3. ....
4. ....

Q2 Peter tested **a mystery component** using a standard test circuit. The table below shows his results.

Voltage (V)	–4.0	–3.0	–2.0	–1.0	0.0	1.0	2.0	3.0	4.0
Component current (A)	0.0	0.0	0.0	0.0	0.0	0.2	1.0	2.0	4.5

a) Draw a **V-I graph** for the component on the axes below.

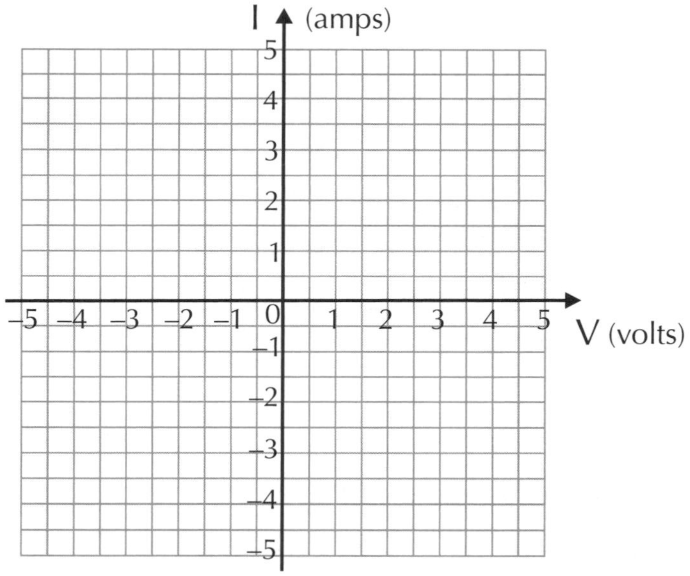

b) Calculate the resistance of the component when a potential difference of **3 V** is applied across it.

....

c) Complete Peter's **conclusions**:

The mystery component is a ....

Top Tips: There are two very important skills you need to master for resistance questions — **interpreting V-I graphs** and using the formula **V = I × R**. Make sure you can do both.

Measuring AC

Q1 Choose from the words below to fill in the gaps.

changing   AC   hertz   DC   volts   direct
alternating   ohms   frequency   amps   direction

In the UK the mains electrical supply is about 230 ....

The supply is .... current (.........) which means that the

.... of the current is constantly ....

The supply has a .... of 50 ....

Q2 Answer the following:

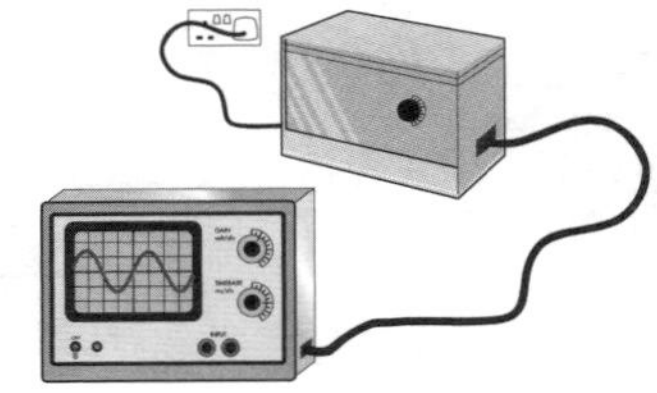

a) What does 'CRO' stand for?

....

b) Which two variables are represented by the axes on a CRO screen?

....

c) Give the names of the two main dials on the front of a CRO.

....

Q3 The diagram shows three traces on the same CRO. The settings are the same in each case.

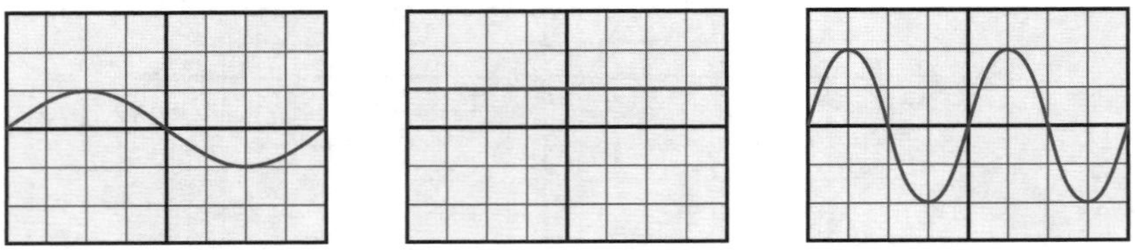

A   B   C

Write down the **letter** of the trace that shows:

a) the highest frequency AC ...., **b)** direct current ...., **c)** the lowest AC voltage ....

Q4 The diagram shows a trace on a CRO screen. The **timebase** is set to 10 ms per division, and the **gain** to 1 volt per division.

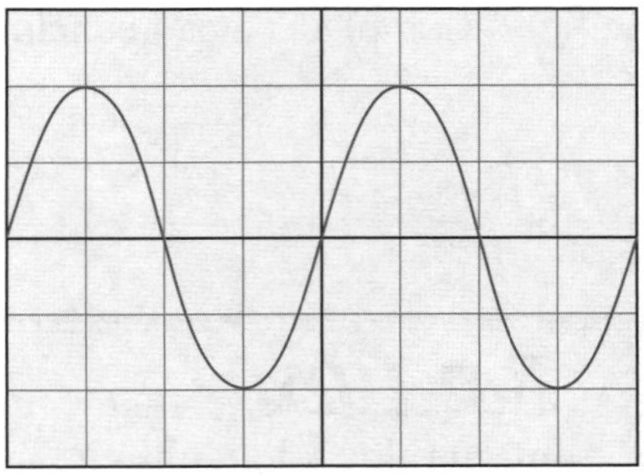

a) What is the peak voltage? ....

b) What is the time period?

....

c) Calculate the frequency of the supply.

....

Series Circuits

Q1 Match up these descriptions with what they describe in a series circuit.

Same everywhere in the circuit	Potential difference
Shared out between the components	Current
The sum of the resistances	Total potential difference
Can be different for each component	Total resistance

Q2 The diagram shows a series circuit.

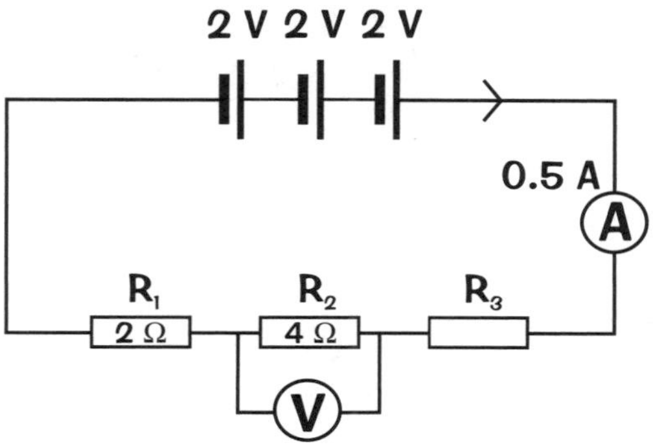

a) Calculate the total potential difference across the battery.

....

b) Work out the total resistance.

....

For parts b) and d), you'll need to use the formula connecting V, I and R.

c) Calculate the resistance of resistor R_3.

....

d) What would you expect the reading on the voltmeter to be?

....

Q3 Gene does an experiment with different numbers of lamps in a series circuit. The diagram below shows his three circuits.

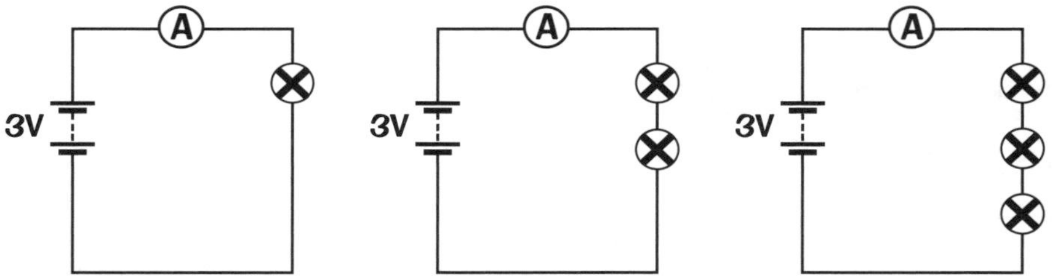

a) What do you think happens to the **brightness** of the lamps as he adds more of them? Explain your answer.

....

....

b) How does the **current** change as more lamps are added? Explain your answer.

....

....

Parallel Circuits

Q1 Indicate whether these statements about parallel circuits are **true** or **false**.

		True	False
a)	Current runs through the components one after another.	☐	☐
b)	Each component has the same potential difference across it.	☐	☐
c)	The current is the same everywhere in the circuit.	☐	☐
d)	It's possible to arrange the components so that they can be switched on and off independently.	☐	☐

Q2 Karen does an experiment with different numbers of lamps in a parallel circuit. The diagrams below show her three circuits.

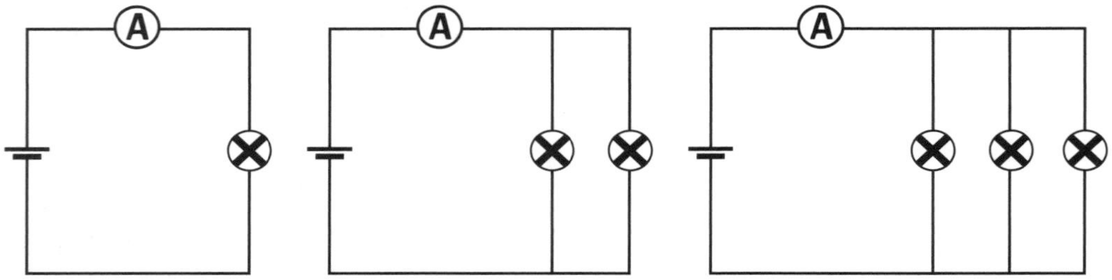

a) What happens to the **brightness** of the lamps as Karen adds more of them? Explain your answer.

....

....

b) One of the lamps in the third circuit is **unscrewed**.
What happens to the brightness of the other lamps?

....

Q3 The diagram opposite shows a **parallel** circuit.

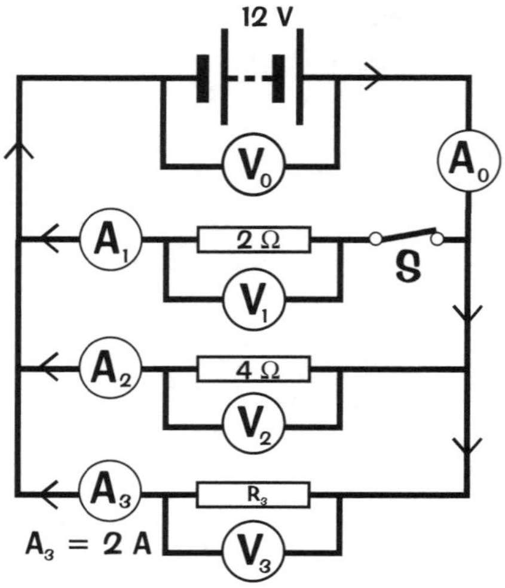

a) Calculate the readings on ammeters:

i) A_1 ....

ii) A_2 ....

b) Find the readings on voltmeters:

i) V_1 ....

ii) V_2 ....

c) What is the resistance of resistor R_3?

....

d) What is the reading on ammeter A_0 when switch S is open?

....

Fuses and Safe Plugs

Q1 Answer the following questions about **plugs**:

a) Why is the body of a plug made of rubber or plastic?

....

b) Explain why some parts of a plug are made from copper or brass.

....

Q2 Use the words below to complete these rules for wiring a plug.

outer   bare   live   earth   neutral   insulation   firmly   green and yellow

a) Strip the .... off the end of each wire.

b) Connect the brown wire to the .... terminal.

c) Connect the blue wire to the .... terminal.

d) Connect the .... wire to the .... terminal.

e) Check all the wires are .... screwed in with no .... bits showing.

f) Fasten the cable grip securely over the .... covering of the cable.

Q3 Put **ticks** in the table to show which wires match each description.

Description	Live	Neutral	Earth
Must always be connected			
Just for safety			
Electricity normally flows in and out of it			
Alternates between +ve and –ve voltage			

Morris thought it best to be earthed at all times — just in case.

Q4 These sentences describe how a **fuse** and **earth wire** work together to help prevent you getting an electric shock from your toaster.

a) Put numbers in the boxes to show the order they should go in. The first one has been done for you.

☐ The surge in current causes the fuse wire to heat up.

☐ Everything is now safe.

1 A fault develops and the earthed casing becomes connected to the live supply.

☐ The live supply is cut off.

☐ The wire melts.

☐ A large current now flows in through the live wire and out through the earth wire.

b) RCCBs can be used in some devices instead of a fuse and earth wire. Give one advantage of using an RCCB over a fuse and earth wire.

....

Energy and Power in Circuits

Q1 Fill in the gaps using the words in the box. You may need to use some words more than once or not at all.

power rating	current	lower	higher	how long	voltage

The total energy transferred by an appliance depends on .... it's used for and its .... The power rating of an appliance can be calculated using the formula: power = ... × ....
The fuse rating for an appliance should be a little .... than the .... the appliance normally draws.

Q2 Calculate the **amount** of electrical energy transformed by the following devices. For each device, say what **forms** of energy most of the electrical energy is converted to.

a) A 100 watt lamp in 10 seconds: .... J.

Electrical energy is converted to .... and .... energy.

b) A 500 W motor in 2 minutes: .... J.

Electrical energy is converted to ...., ... and .... energy.

c) A 1 kW heater in 20 seconds: .... J.

Electrical energy is converted to .... energy.

Remember to put time in seconds and power in W.

d) A 2 kW heater in 10 minutes: .... J.

Electrical energy is converted to .... energy.

Q3 Lucy is comparing **three lamps**. She connects each lamp in a circuit and measures the **current**. Her results are shown in the table below.

	Lamp A	Lamp B	Lamp C
Voltage across lamp (V)	12	3	230
Current through lamp (A)	2.5	4	0.1
Power (W)			
Energy used in one minute (J)			

a) Complete the table by filling in the missing values.

b) What rating of fuse would each lamp need? (Choose from 2 A, 3 A, 5 A, 7 A or 13 A.)

A = ..., B = ..., C = ...

Top Tips: Anything which supplies electricity is supplying **electrical energy**, which can be converted to other forms of energy — like heat or light. Remember that. And there are two **important formulas** for you to learn — P = I × V and P = E × t.

Charge, Voltage and Energy Change

Q1 A 3 volt battery can supply a current of 5 amps for 20 minutes before it needs recharging.

a) Calculate:

i) the number of seconds in 20 minutes.

....

ii) how much charge the battery can provide before it needs recharging.

....

b) Each coulomb of charge from the battery can carry 3 J of energy.
How much energy can the battery transform before it needs recharging?

....

Q2 Sally is comparing two lamps, A and B. She takes the measurements shown in the table.

	Lamp A	Lamp B
Current through lamp (A)	2	4
Voltage drop across lamp (V)	3	2
Charge passing in 10 s (C)		
Energy transformed in 10 s (J)		

Calculate the **missing values** and write them in the table.

Q3 The motor in a fan is attached to a 9 V battery.
A current of 4 A flows through the motor for 7 minutes.

a) Calculate the total charge passed.

....

b) Calculate the energy transformed by the motor.

....

Q4 The following statements are wrong.
Write out a correct version of each.

Look back at the formulas for charge and energy if you're puzzled.

a) Higher voltage means more coulombs of charge per second.

....

b) One ampere (amp) is the same as one coulomb per joule.

....

c) One volt is the same as one joule per ampere.

....

Relative Speed and Velocity

Q1 **Speed cameras** can be used to detect speeding motorists. The section of road in the diagram below has a **speed limit of 50 miles per hour**.

a) 1 mile = 1609 metres. Show that 50 miles per hour is about the same speed as 22 m/s.

....

b) The diagram below shows a car passing in front of a speed camera. The two pictures show the position of the car 0.5 s apart. The distance between each white line on the road is 5 metres. (The diagram is not to scale.)

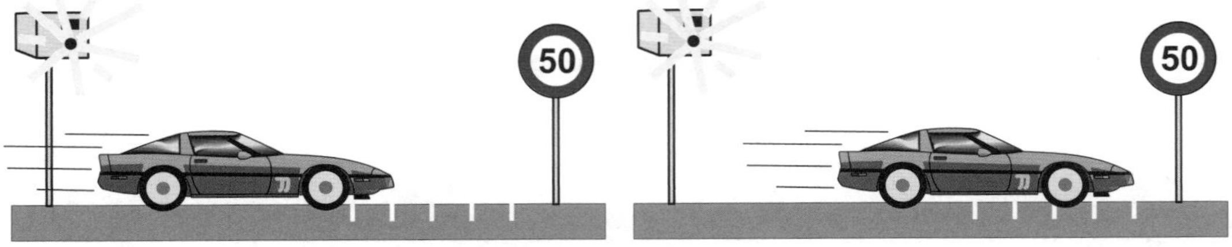

Was the car breaking the speed limit? Show your working.

....

....

Q2 Use the words in the box to complete the following passage.

scalar	direction	vector	speed	shape	force	temperature

A quantity that only has a number is a .... quantity.
Examples of this include .... and ....
A quantity like velocity has a number and a .... This is known as a ....

Q3 **Two aeroplanes** are flying in **opposite directions** at **different speeds**.

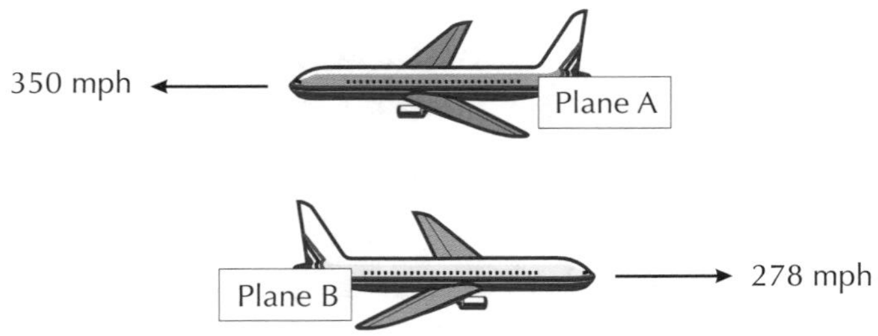

How fast is plane A travelling relative to plane B?

....

Combining Velocities and Forces

Q1 Work out the size and direction of the **resultant force** acting on the pots of jam shown below.

a) 

Size of force .... N

Direction: ....

b) 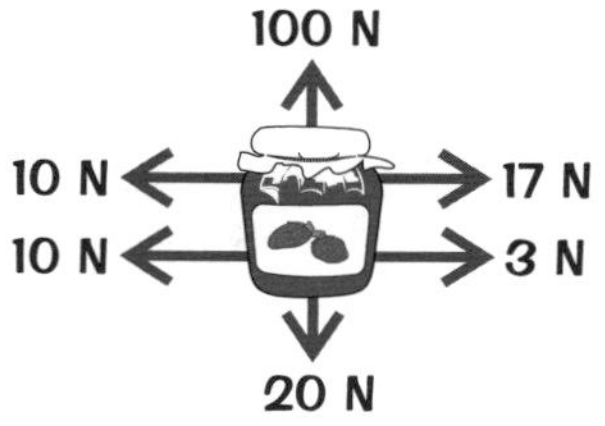

Size of force .... N

Direction: ....

Q2 Greta swims at **1 m/s** to the **East** along a river. Ray stands on the riverbank and watches her.

a) How fast is Greta swimming relative to Ray if the river is flowing at **1.5 m/s due East**?

Velocity = ... m/s Direction = ...

b) How fast is Greta swimming relative to Ray if the river is flowing **2.0 m/s due West**?

Velocity = ... m/s Direction = ...

Q3 Forces and velocities can be combined in **vector diagrams**.

a) A glider is flying at **10 m/s due North** when it experiences a cross wind of **15 m/s due East**. Complete the vector diagram and use it to work out the resultant velocity of the glider — its speed and its new bearing (angle clockwise from North). Give your answers to the nearest whole number.

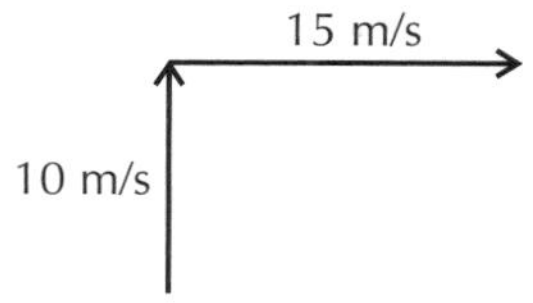

....

....

....

Resultant velocity = ... m/s on a bearing of ....°

b) Emma swims across a river which is flowing westwards at 5 m/s. She swims at 2 m/s, heading directly across the river from point X.

Calculate Emma's resultant velocity — her speed and the angle between her direction of travel and the river bank. Give your answers to the nearest m/s and the nearest degree.

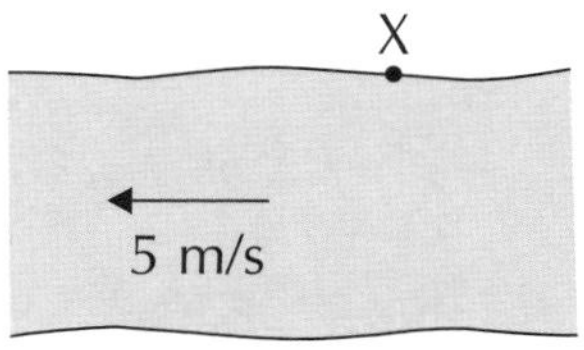

....

....

....

Equations of Motion

Q1 a) What quantities do the following symbols stand for in the **equations of motion**?

i) **s** stands for ....

ii) **u** stands for ....

iii) **v** stands for ....

iv) **t** stands for ....

v) **a** stands for ....

You should always stand for the national anthem.

b) Complete the four equations below.

s = ut +	s = ——— t	v = +	v^2 =

Q2 Choose the appropriate equation and solve the following.

You'll need to rearrange the equation for some of these.

a) Find **s** if u = 0 m/s, a = 5 m/s^2 and t = 20 s. ....

....

b) Find **v** if u = 20 m/s, a = 1 m/s^2 and s = 250 m. ....

....

c) Find **t** if s = 45 m, u = 3 m/s and v = 15 m/s.

....

....

d) Find **a** if s = 100 m, u = 0 m/s and t = 5 s.

....

....

Q3 A car accelerates at 2.5 m/s^2 from rest. What **speed** will it have reached after 20 seconds?

....

....

Q4 I throw a banana vertically up into the air at an initial speed of 10 m/s. It accelerates downwards at 10 m/s^2. Calculate the **maximum height** of the banana.

....

....

....

Take 'up' as positive and think about the speed the banana is going at when it reaches its maximum height.

Projectile Motion

Q1 Choose from the words below to complete the passage.

friction gravity ground track parabola trajectory hyperbola

The only force acting on a projectile is .... (ignoring air resistance). The path a projectile follows is called its .... The shape of this path is a ....

Q2 For each of these statements, tick **true** or **false** as appropriate.

		True	False
a)	Horizontal and vertical motion don't affect one another.	☐	☐
b)	A bullet fired horizontally at 200 m/s will accelerate down to the ground at the same rate as a stone thrown horizontally at 1 m/s. (Ignore air resistance.)	☐	☐
c)	If something is thrown horizontally at 10 m/s, its initial vertical velocity is 10 m/s.	☐	☐
d)	The horizontal velocity remains constant for a projectile (ignoring air resistance).	☐	☐

Q3 This diagram shows a **regular** pulse of water droplets that have been **projected** through the air.

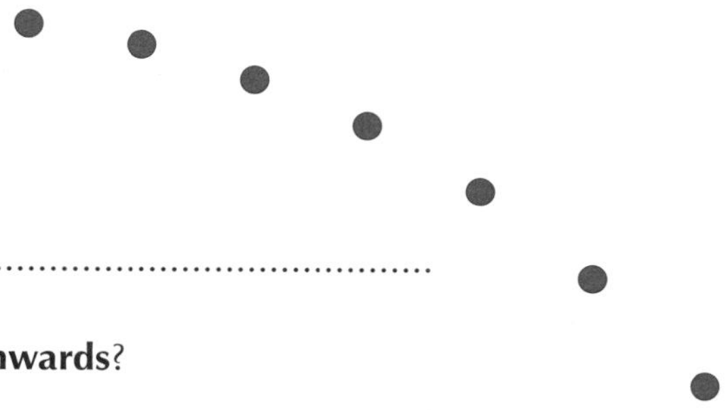

a) How can you tell from the diagram that the **horizontal velocity** is **constant**?

....

b) How can you tell that the droplets are **accelerating downwards**?

....

Q4 Which of the following are examples of projectile motion? Circle any which are.

a football kicked towards the goal

an orange rolling off a table

a cannonball fired from a cannon

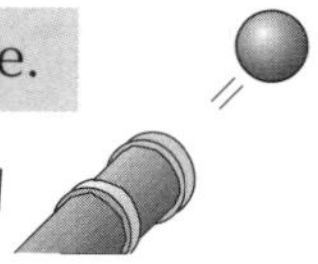

a powered plane flying over the Himalayas

a football dribbled towards the goal

a high jumper in flight

Q5 A plane is carrying some water to try and put out a forest fire. The plane is flying **horizontally** at a velocity of **80 m/s** and it is **125 m** above the ground.

a) Taking the acceleration due to gravity to be **10 m/s²**, how long will it take the water to reach the ground once it has left the plane (ignoring air resistance)?

....

....

b) Ignoring air resistance, at what distance before the forest fire must the water be released?

....

Turning Forces and Centre of Mass

Q1 a) Fill in the blanks in the following passage, using the words supplied.

pivot	perpendicular	moment	force

The turning effect of a .... is called its ....
It can be found by multiplying the force by the .... distance from the line of action of the force to the ....

b) What are the units in which moments are measured? ....

Q2 To open a door, its handle needs to be **rotated clockwise.**

a) A force of 45 N is exerted vertically downwards on the door-handle at a distance of 0.1 m from the pivot. What is the **moment** of the force?

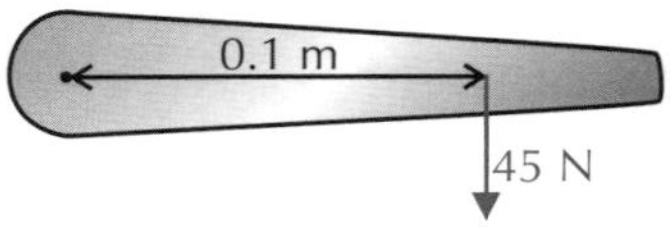

....

b) Pictures **A**, **B**, **C** and **D** show equal forces being exerted on the handle.

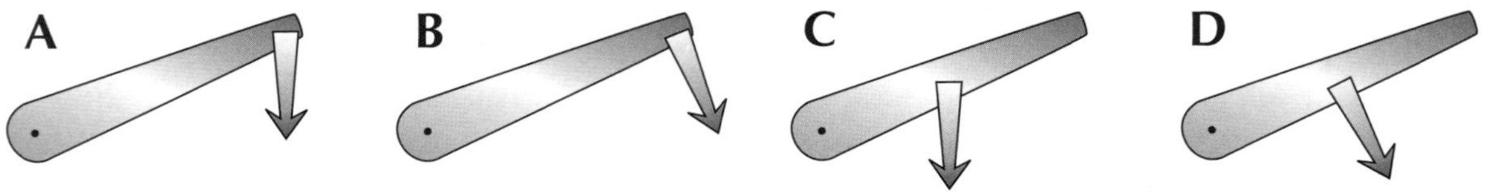

Which of the forces shown (**A**, **B**, **C** or **D**) exerts:

i) the largest moment? ....

ii) the smallest moment? ....

Q3 Barry the burglar plans to use a crowbar to force open the door of his neighbour's house. He has calculated that a moment of **30 Nm** will be enough to force the door open.

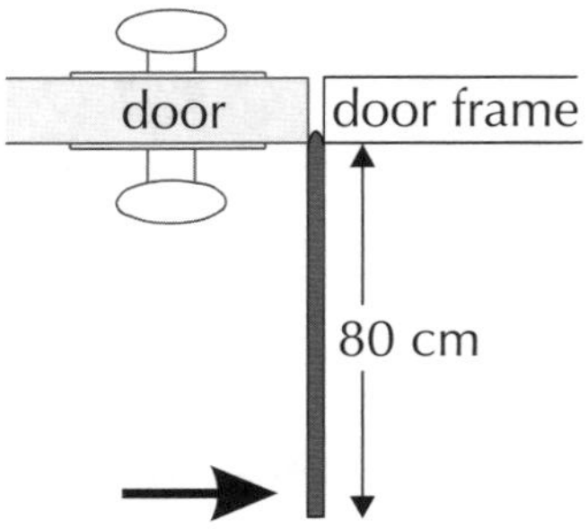

a) Barry's only crowbar is **80 cm** long, and he can exert a force on it of up to **45 N**. Will he be able to force the door (by pushing on the crowbar in the direction shown)? Explain your reasoning.

....

....

b) Jez, Barry's partner in crime, can only exert a force of **35 N**. He realises that he'd need a longer crowbar than Barry's. What's the **minimum length** of crowbar Jez would need to force the door?

....

....

Turning Forces and Centre of Mass

Q4 A baby's pram toy consists of a toy banana hanging from a bar over the pram.

a) The banana is hanging **at rest**, as shown.
Draw a line on which the centre of mass **must** fall.

b) Complete the following sentences by choosing from the words and phrases below:

level with	**vertically below**	**perpendicular**	**moment**	**centre of mass**	**horizontal**

When a suspended object's .... is .... the pivot, the .... distance between the line of action of the gravitational force and the pivot is zero. This means that there is no .... due to the object's weight.

Q5 You can think of the **centre of mass** as the point where all the weight of an object acts.

a) Using lines of symmetry, find the centre of mass of each of these shapes:

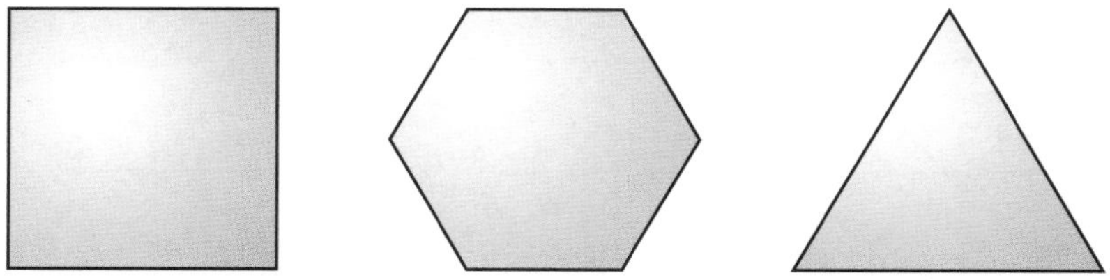

b) **Circle** the correct answer to complete this sentence.
The centre of mass of a raindrop is:

A at the top

B near the top

C midway down

D near the bottom

E at the bottom

Turning Forces and Centre of Mass

Q6 Two men, one at each end, hold a 0.8 m long metal pole weighing 130 N so that it is in a **horizontal** position. One man accidentally lets go of his end.

What is the moment on the pole due to its weight an instant after he lets go?

First, find the centre of mass of the pole.

Draw a diagram here to help you.

Q7 Some pupils want to find the centre of mass of an **irregularly shaped** piece of cardboard. They are equipped with a stand to hang the card from, a plumb line and a pencil. They make a hole near one edge of the card and hang it from the stand.

a) What steps should they take next in order to find the centre of mass?

b) How could they make their result more reliable?

Top Tips: Moments aren't too bad — there's only one formula to learn, but remember that it only works when the force and distance are at right angles. Finding centre of mass is a bit more of a faff (unless the shape's nice and regular) — make sure you learn the method good and proper.

Balanced Moments and Stability

Q1 A 2 N weight (Weight A) sits 20 cm to the left of the pivot of a balance.
A 5 N weight (Weight B) is placed 16 cm to the left of the pivot.

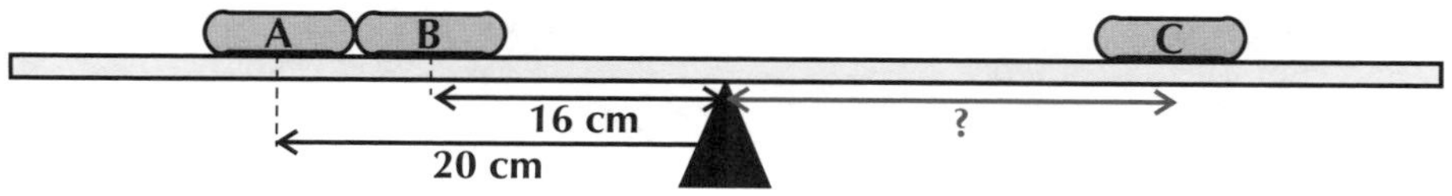

a) What is the moment exerted by **Weight A**? ....

b) What is the moment exerted by **Weight B**? ....

c) How far to the right of the pivot should Weight C (8 N) be placed to **balance** A and B?

....

....

d) If all three of the weights were exactly **twice as far** away from the pivot, would the balance tip over to one side? Explain your answer.

....

Q2 The top drawer of a two-drawer filing cabinet is full of heavy files, but the bottom drawer is empty.

Why is the cabinet in danger of falling over if the top drawer is fully pulled out?

....

....

Q3 The pictures show three different designs for **vases**.

Which vase will be **most stable**? Explain your answer.

....

....

Q4 One side of a drop-leaf table is pivoted on a hinge and supported 5 cm from its edge by a table leg. The table leaf is 80 cm long and weighs 40 N.

Find the force, F, exerted by the table leg (when the table leaf is fully extended).

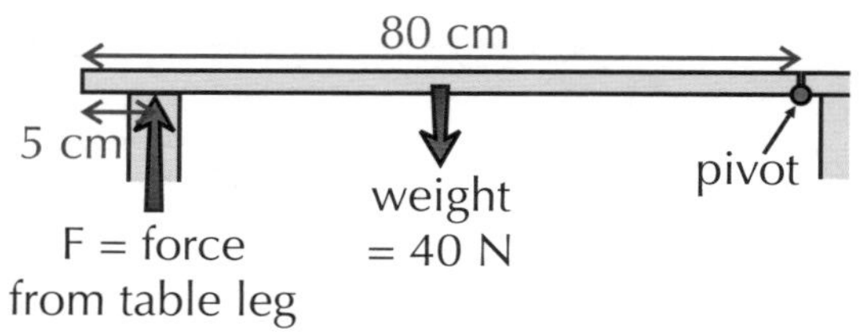

....

....

Circular Motion

Q1 Which of the following is the **best definition** of acceleration? Circle the appropriate letter.

A an increase in speed

B a change in direction

C an increase in velocity

D a change in velocity

E a change in speed

Q2 The diagram below shows a clock with hands that move **steadily** around the clock-face.

a) Draw and label with 'A' an arrow on the diagram to show the direction of the **velocity** of the tip of the **minute hand**.

b) Draw and label with 'B' an arrow to show the direction of the **acceleration** of the tip of the **hour hand**.

Q3 A **satellite** orbiting the Earth travels at a constant speed.

a) Is the satellite accelerating? Explain your answer.

....

b) Put a tick next to each true statement below.

☐ "If a body is accelerating then there must be a resultant force acting on it."

☐ "The forces acting on a body going round in a circle at a steady speed must be balanced."

☐ "If there is no resultant force acting on a body then it carries on moving in a straight line at the same speed."

c) What is the general name for a force that keeps a body moving in a circular path?

....

d) Draw lines to match up the following bodies with the force that keeps them moving in a circle.

A runner running round a circular track	Gravity
A satellite in orbit round the Earth	Tension
The seats at the ends of the spokes of a spinning fairground ride	Friction

Q4 Circle the correct options in these sentences.

a) The greater the mass of a body, the **smaller / greater** the force needed to keep it moving in a circle.

b) It takes a greater force to keep a body moving in a **smaller / larger** circle.

c) A cyclist rides round a circular track at a speed of 20 m/s.
The frictional force between his tyres and the track is 1467 N.
He speeds up to 21 m/s — the frictional force changes to **1617 N / 1331 N**.

Satellites

Q1 Some satellites have **geosynchronous orbits**. Others have **polar** orbits.

a) Complete the following by circling the correct words.

A geosynchronous satellite is in a low / high orbit over the Earth's equator / poles.

b) On the diagram, draw the orbits of a polar satellite and a geosynchronous satellite.

Label the polar orbit '**P**' and the geosynchronous orbit '**G**'.

Q2 Satellites have lots of uses. **Different types** of satellite are needed for different applications.

a) Explain how a satellite in **low polar orbit** can scan the whole surface of the globe in a day.

....

....

b) Give one use of low polar orbiting satellites.

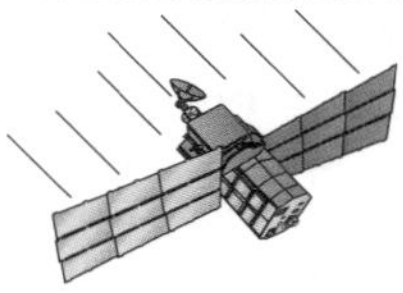

....

c) Tick **true** or **false** for each of these statements.

	True	False
i) All geostationary satellites take the same time to make one orbit.	☐	☐
ii) A geostationary orbit must pass above the equator.	☐	☐
iii) A geostationary orbit must pass above the poles.	☐	☐
iv) A geostationary satellite can orbit in any direction.	☐	☐

d) Are artificial satellites outside the influence of Earth's gravity? How do you know?

....

Q3 Answer the following questions on **geosynchronous** orbits.

a) Why is it useful for a **communications** satellite to be in a **geosynchronous** orbit?

....

b) How long does a **geosynchronous** satellite take to make **one** complete orbit of the Earth?

....

c) There is enough space to put more than 400 satellites in a geosynchronous orbit. In practice, why wouldn't we be able to use more than about 400 geostationary satellites?

....

Gravity and Orbits

Q1 In the solar system, each planet's orbit is a slightly different **shape** and the planets all move at different **speeds**.

a) Complete the following passage, choosing from the words in the box.

orbit	energy	galaxy	nearer	gravity	distance

A planet moving past a star has its path pulled into a curve by the star's .... If the planet is moving at just the right speed its path will come back on itself and form an .... To stay in orbit at a particular ...., a planet must move at a particular speed.

b) Which move **faster**, planets closer to the Sun or planets further away from the Sun?

....

Q2 This is a diagram of a **planet** orbiting the Sun.

a) Draw an arrow on the diagram to show the direction of the Sun's **gravitational force** on the planet and label it 'F'.

b) Now draw an arrow showing the direction of the planet's **velocity** and label it 'V'.

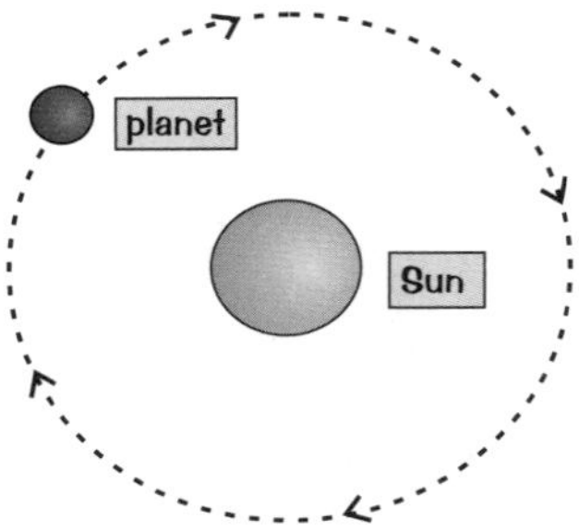

Q3 Here is a diagram of a **comet**'s orbit around the Sun. **A**, **B**, **C** and **D** are different points on the orbit.

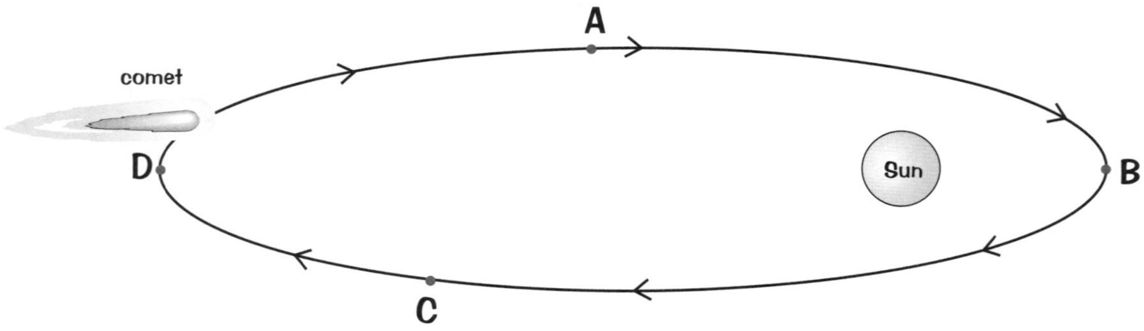

a) Out of the points A-D on the orbit, at which point is the comet travelling:

i) most slowly? ....

ii) most quickly? ....

b) Explain why the speed of the comet changes in different parts of its orbit.

....

....

Gravity and Orbits

Q4 The table below contains data about the orbits of six of the planets which orbit the Sun.

A.U. = astronomical unit — the distance from the Earth to the Sun.

	Mercury	Venus	Earth	Mars	Jupiter	Saturn
Distance from Sun (A.U)	0.39	0.72	1.00	1.52	5.20	9.54
Time for one orbit (Earth years)	0.24	0.62	1.00	1.88	11.9	29.5

a) What can you conclude from the data? Circle the letters of any of the following which apply.

A The further out the planet is from the Sun, the weaker the Sun's gravity.

B The time it takes a planet to orbit the Sun is directly proportional to its distance from the Sun.

C The further out the planet is from the Sun, the longer it takes to orbit.

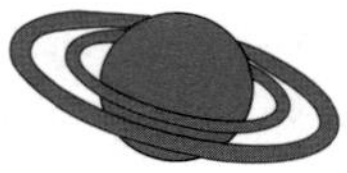

D Planets further out than Saturn will take longer than 29.5 years to orbit the Sun.

b) Why are the orbits of geostationary satellites higher up than those of polar satellites?

....

....

Q5 The force of gravity between two objects depends on their masses and the distance between them.

a) If you double the distance you are from a planet, what happens to the force of its gravity on you?

....

b) A satellite orbiting the Earth feels a gravitational force of **250 N**.
What gravitational force would the same satellite feel if its orbit were moved to be:

i) five times further away from the Earth?

....

....

ii) half the distance from the Earth?

....

....

Top Tips: Watch out with that old inverse square law. Don't forget the 'square' bit, or the 'inverse' bit — it's easy to rush things and end up making a mistake. It's the inverse square law that explains why comets move the way they do, in those long orbits.

Magnetic Fields

Q1 Fill in the word **north** or **south** in the following sentences.

a) A .... pole will repel a north pole.

b) The arrows on field lines are always directed towards the .... pole of the field.

c) Reversing the current in a solenoid will turn a .... pole into a south pole.

Q2 The diagram below shows a **wire** carrying a current passing through a piece of **flat card**.

a) Some **iron filings** are sprinkled onto the card. When the current is switched on, a pattern develops in the iron filings.

On the diagram, sketch the pattern the iron filings make, including arrows to show the direction of the magnetic field.

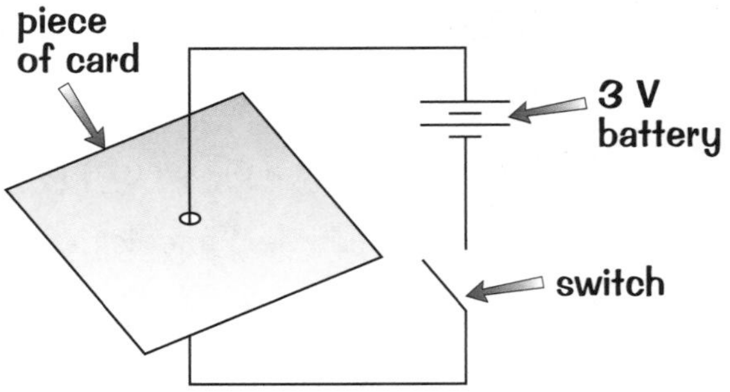

Remember the direction of conventional current flow. Then use your hand...

b) A loop of current-carrying wire as shown has a **stronger** magnetic field **inside** the loop than outside. Explain why this is, including a sketch of the magnetic field.

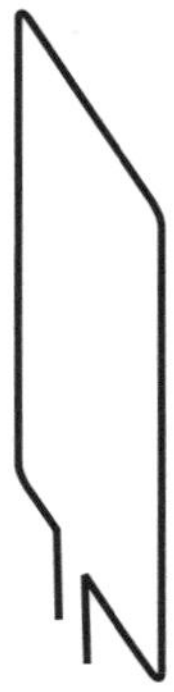

....

....

....

Q3 Tick to show whether the following are **true** or **false**. Write a correct version of each false statement.

	True	False
a) Inside a solenoid, the magnetic field is just like a bar magnet's.	☐	☐
b) The iron core of an electromagnet keeps its magnetism when the current is switched off.	☐	☐
c) As more turns are added to a current-carrying coil its magnetic field gets weaker.	☐	☐
d) Adding a soft iron core to a solenoid will increase the strength of its magnetic field.	☐	☐

Magnetic Fields

Q4 The diagram below shows a **solenoid**.

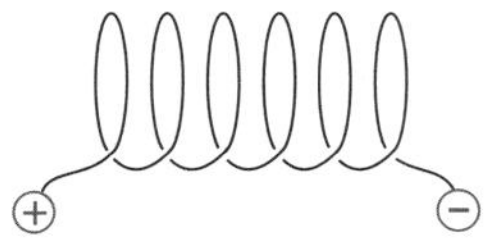

a) Draw the shape of the magnetic field around the solenoid.

b) Indicate on the diagram the **north** and **south** poles of the solenoid.

c) What effect would the solenoid have on a piece of soft iron placed near one of its ends?

....

d) Sarah holds a bar magnet with its north pole nearest to the left hand end of the coil in the diagram. The bar magnet experiences a force.

i) In what direction would the force on the bar magnet be — towards the coil or away from it?

....

ii) Suggest **two** different ways in which the direction of this force could be reversed.

....

....

Q5 Explain why the following are **bad ideas**.

a) Making an electromagnetic crane out of a **magnetically hard** material, like steel.

....

....

b) Reversing the current in **both** of a pair of solenoids to stop them repelling each other.

....

....

Top Tips: Make sure you always draw **magnetic field arrows** going the right way. It's easy to lose marks on fiddly bits like that when you aren't paying attention. And don't go using the wrong **hand** to work out the field around a current-carrying wire — cos you'll get it **wrong** if you do that.

The Motor Effect

Q1 Complete the passage below using the words supplied.

force field angle stronger permanent current magnetic magnets

A wire carrying an electric current has a .... around it. This can react with the magnetic fields of other wires or of .... to produce a .... and sometimes movement. A bigger .... or a .... magnet will produce a bigger force. The size of the force also depends on the .... at which the two magnetic fields meet.

Q2 The diagram shows an electrical wire between two magnetic poles.
When the current is switched on, the wire moves at **right angles** to the magnetic field.

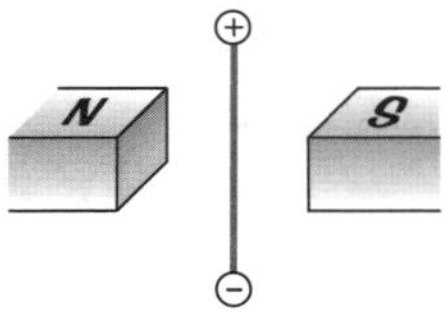

a) Which way will the wire move?

....

b) How could the wire be made to move in the opposite direction? ....

c) Explain **why** the wire moves.

....

....

Q3 This experiment was set up to illustrate the motor effect.
When the current is switched on the bar rolls along the rails.

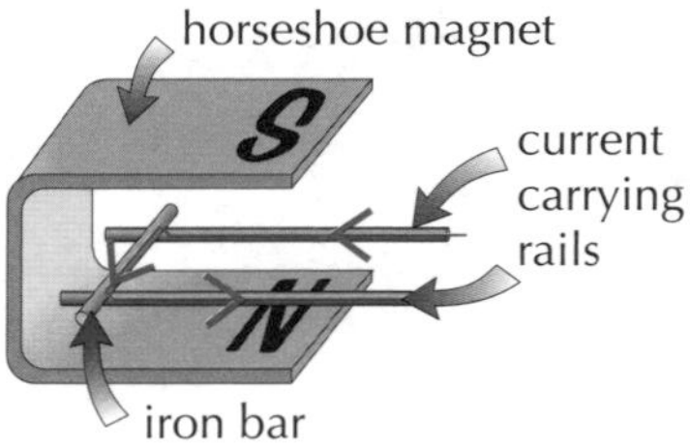

a) Which of the statements A to D below states correctly what the experiment shows? Circle the appropriate letter.

A A force acts in the same direction as the current is flowing.
B The magnetic field from the magnet combines with the field from the current in the bar.
C The horseshoe magnet pushes the bar along.
D The current in the bar pulls it along the rails.

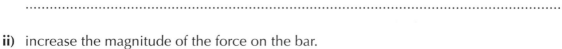

b) Give two changes you could make to the experiment to:

i) reverse the direction of the force on the bar.

....

....

ii) increase the magnitude of the force on the bar.

....

The Simple Electric Motor

Q1 Which of the following will make an electric motor spin **faster**? Circle the relevant letter(s).

A Having more turns on the coil.

B Using a stronger magnetic field.

C Using a soft iron core.

D Using a bigger current.

E Using a commutator.

Q2 Read the three statements below. Tick the box next to each statement that you think is **true**.

☐ The split ring commutator makes the motor spin faster.

☐ The split ring commutator reverses the direction of the current every half turn by swapping the contacts to the DC supply.

☐ The split ring commutator reverses the polarity of the DC supply every half turn.

Q3 Suggest two ways in which the direction of spin of a simple DC motor can be reversed.

....

....

Q4 An electric motor is often used in lifts in tall buildings and mines.
Describe briefly how an electric motor can be used to raise (or lower) a lift cage.

....

....

....

Q5 The diagram shows a current-carrying coil in a magnetic field as part of a simple motor.

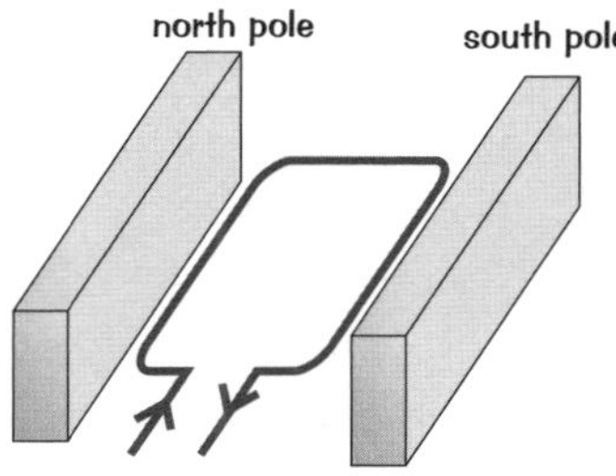

a) Describe the direction of the force on the **left-hand** arm of the coil.

....

b) In a practical motor, the poles of the magnet are **curved**. Explain why.

....

....

....

Generators

Q1 Choose from the words below to complete the passage.

brushes field current direction drier half full motors slip split magnetic tumble
In a generator, a coil is made to turn inside a .... As the coil spins a .... is induced in it. An AC generator has .... rings and .... They produce current which changes .... every .... turn of the coil.

Q2 **Slip rings** are an important part of both generators and dynamos.
Which of the statements below about slip rings in a generator are **true**?
Tick the appropriate box(es).

☐ The slip rings provide current to an external circuit in the opposite direction every full turn.

☐ The slip rings reverse the direction of the current supplied to an external circuit every half turn.

☐ The slip rings enable the current to enter and leave the coils of the generator while it is turning.

Q3 Explain why the lights on a bicycle with a dynamo dim if the bicycle goes more slowly.

....

....

....

Q4 Here is a **CRO display** of the voltage produced by a **generator**.

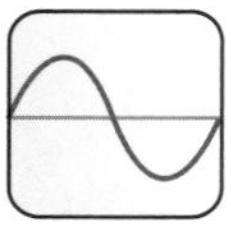

The displays below show the voltage produced by the same generator under **different conditions**.

<u>**Traces on oscilloscope**</u>

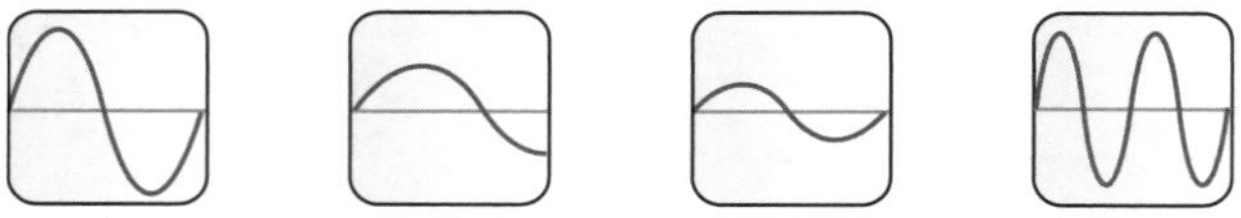

A **B** **C** **D**

Pick the correct letter A-D to show:

a) The generator turning **twice as fast**. ....

b) The generator turning **more slowly** than originally. ....

c) The generator turning at the **same speed** as originally but with **stronger magnets**. ....

Transformers

Q1 Number the following statements in the right order to explain how a transformer works.

	This causes a rapidly changing magnetic field in the core.
	An alternating current can flow in a circuit connected to the secondary coil.
	An alternating current flows in the primary coil.
1	An alternating voltage is connected to the primary coil of a transformer.
	The changing magnetic field induces an alternating voltage in the secondary coil.

Q2 Look at the diagram to the right showing two electrical circuits.

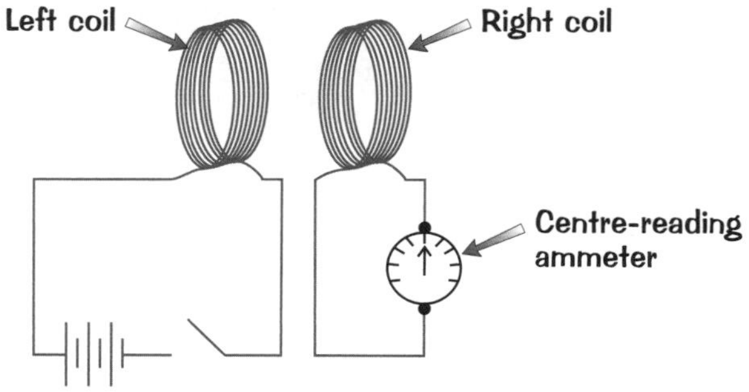

When the switch is closed, a deflection is seen on the ammeter and then the needle returns to zero. When the switch is opened again, a deflection is seen in the opposite direction.

a) Explain why this happens.

....

....

b) What could you add to the apparatus to make the needle move further?

....

Q3 Tick the boxes to indicate whether the following statements are **true** or **false**.

		True	False
a)	Step-up transformers have more turns on the primary coil than the secondary coil.	☐	☐
b)	The iron core conducts the current from the primary coil to the secondary coil.	☐	☐
c)	When a transformer is working it behaves as though a bar magnet was being repeatedly pushed into and pulled out of the secondary coil.	☐	☐
d)	If you put a DC into the primary coil, a DC will be produced in the secondary coil.	☐	☐

Q4 A transformer is needed to change 230 V to 23 V. If it has 2000 turns on its primary coil, how many turns would the transformer need on its secondary coil?

....

....

Q5 A transformer has 100 turns on its primary coil and 4000 turns on its secondary coil. What **input voltage** would produce an output voltage of 10 000 V?

....

....

Transformers

Q6 Isolating transformers are safety devices.

a) Which sentence correctly states the relationship between the primary and secondary coils of an isolating transformer? Circle the correct letter.

A An isolating transformer has **more** turns on the **primary** coil than on the secondary coil.

B An isolating transformer has **equal** numbers of turns on the primary and secondary coils.

C An isolating transformer has **more** turns on the **secondary** coil than on the primary coil.

b) Explain why an isolating transformer is often used in a **bathroom shaver circuit**.

....

....

....

Q7 About 8.5% of electricity generated in the UK is lost before it reaches homes and businesses.

a) How is energy 'lost' in the National Grid?

....

b) The power lost in an electrical circuit depends on the current and the resistance of the wires. Use the formulas **P = VI** and **V = IR** to find a formula for power lost in terms of current and resistance.

....

....

c) A step-up transformer increases the voltage. What does it do to the current?

....

d) Work out the current when 1 MW of power is transmitted at:

i) 250 V ....

ii) 250 000 V ....

e) Use your answers to **a)-d)** to explain fully why and how transformers are used in the National Grid.

....

....

....

....

....

Nuclear Power

Q1 The diagram below shows how energy from a gas-cooled nuclear reactor generates electricity.

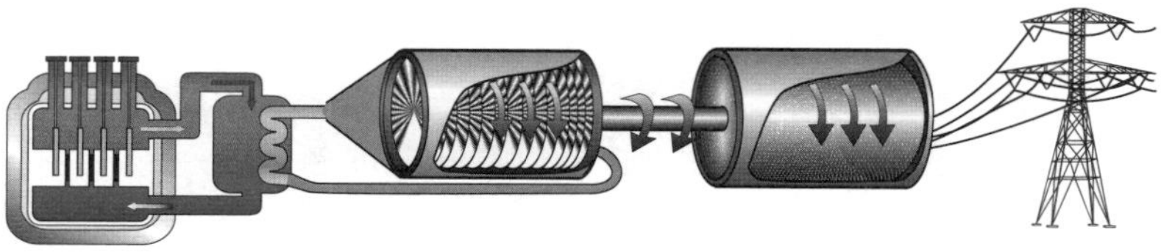

a) Describe how heat energy from the reactor is used to generate electricity.

....

....

b) **i)** Explain how the control rods control the rate of fission.

....

....

ii) What material are control rods usually made from? ....

c) Why is the reactor surrounded with a very thick layer of concrete?

....

Q2 Nuclear power is an example of how nuclear fission can be used **peacefully**.

a) Give one **destructive** use of nuclear fission.

....

b) How is the chain reaction different in this case from that in a reactor?

....

Q3 Explain how a nuclear fission **chain reaction** occurs, starting with a single **plutonium** nucleus absorbing a **slow-moving neutron**.

....

....

....

....

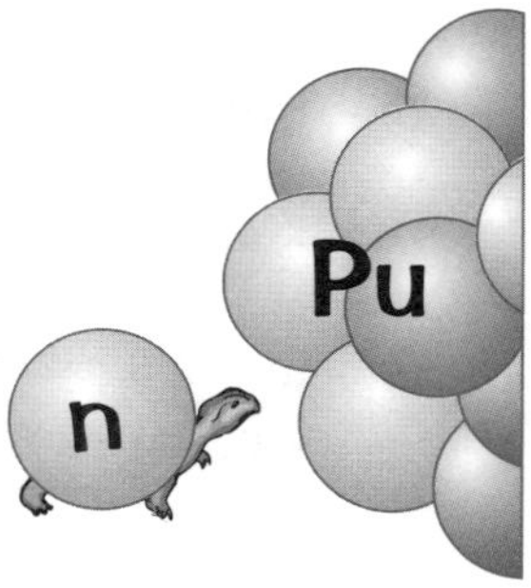

Nuclear Power and Fusion

Q1   Radioactive waste left over from **nuclear fission** is very difficult to dispose of.

    a)   Why is the waste produced by nuclear power stations such a long-term problem?

    ....

    b)   Describe one way of disposing of high-level radioactive waste.

    ....

    ....

Q2   Indicate whether the following statements are **true** or **false**.
Write out correct versions of any false statements.

	True	False
a) Nuclear fusion involves small nuclei joining together.	☐	☐
b) A nuclear fission reaction releases more energy than a nuclear fusion reaction.	☐	☐
c) Fusion reactors produce lots of radioactive waste.	☐	☐
d) Only a few experimental fusion reactors are generating electricity.	☐	☐

    ....

    ....

    ....

Q3   The energy released in stars comes from fusion.

    a)   Write down one condition needed for fusion to take place. ....

    b)   Fusion reactors are extremely hard to build.

        i)   Why can the 'fuel' used not be held in a physical container?

        ....

        ii)   How are fusion reactors built to get around this problem?

        ....

    c)   Explain in terms of energy input and output why fusion reactors aren't in widespread use yet.

    ....

    d)   In 1989 two scientists claimed to have released energy through **cold fusion**.
Suggest why the report caused such excitement.

    ....

    ....

Images

Q1 Images formed by mirrors or lenses can either be **real** or **virtual**.

a) What is the difference between a real and a virtual image?

b) State whether the following images are real or virtual:

i) an image you see in a plane mirror.

ii) an image formed on the retina of your eye.

iii) an image you see when looking through a magnifying glass.

c) What **three** pieces of information do you need to give to describe the nature of an image?

Q2 The diagram shows a **pinhole camera**. Light reflected from a goat passes through a pinhole to form an image on a tissue paper screen.

Draw rays from the top and bottom of the object showing how the image is formed.

Q3 Light can be both **reflected** and **refracted**.

a) In answer to a physics question, Harold writes: "I know that no reflection occurs when I look at a wall because if the wall reflected any light I'd see my reflection in it." Explain why he is wrong.

b) What is the relationship between the angle of incidence and the angle of reflection?

c) What does it mean when we say that a beam of light **refracts** when it enters a different medium?

d) What causes refraction? Circle one of these alternatives.

A Refraction is caused by an image being formed at the boundary between two media.

B Refraction is caused by light being reflected off the boundary between two media.

C Refraction is caused by one medium being better able to absorb light than another.

D Refraction is caused by light changing speed as it enters another medium.

Mirrors

Q1 The diagram below shows a pencil being reflected in a **plane mirror**. Some of the rays have already been drawn in.

a) On the diagram, draw in the rays showing how light is reflected to form an image of the **top** of the pencil.

b) Is the image in a plane mirror real or virtual?

....

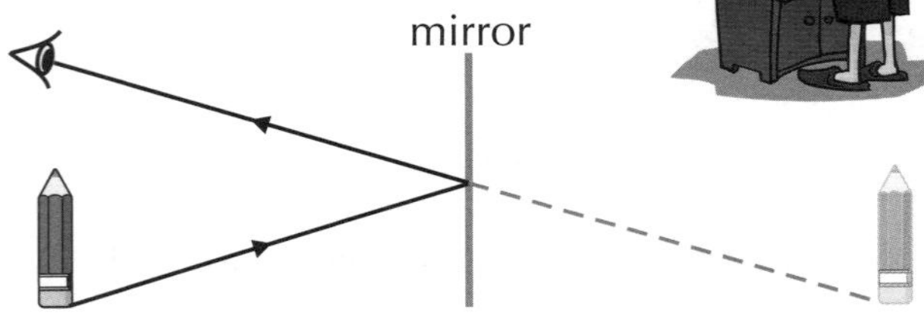

Q2 Below are four sentences about **curved** mirrors. Put them in the correct spaces in the table.

Reflective on outside of curve. **Reflected light converges.**
Reflective on inside of curve. **Reflected light diverges.**

	Description	Behaviour of parallel rays shining on mirror
Concave mirror		
Convex mirror		

Q3 The diagram below shows a curved mirror.

On the diagram, label the:

axis,

focal point,

vertex,

centre of curvature.

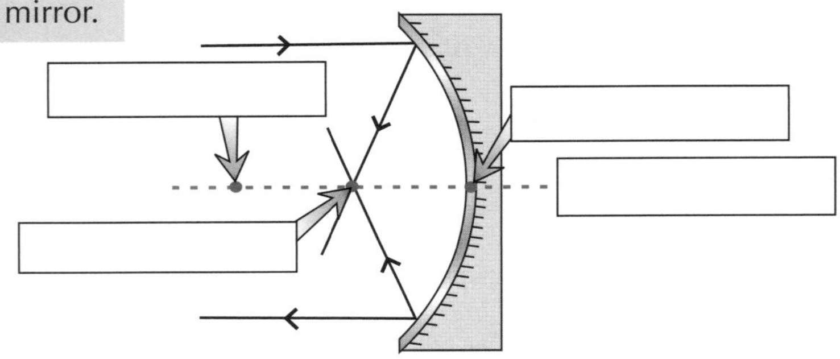

Q4 The diagram below shows an object in front of a uniform concave mirror. F is the focal point.

a) What happens to an incident ray that passes through the **focal point**?

....

....

....

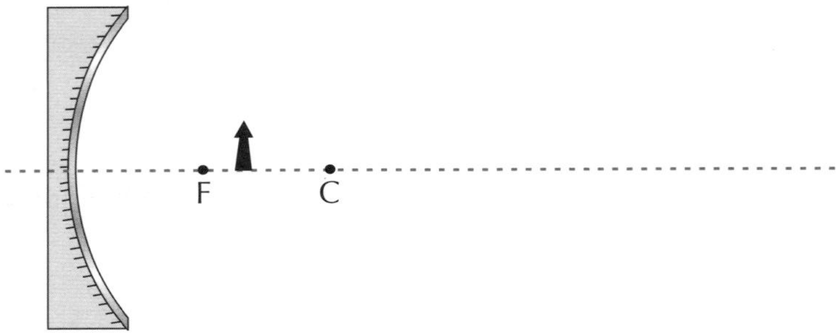

b) On the diagram, draw rays to construct an image of the object (the arrow shape).

c) The object is moved steadily along the axis, away from the mirror, until it reaches a point to the **right** of the **centre of curvature** (C) of the mirror.

i) Describe what happens to the **size** of the image as the object is moved past C.

....

ii) Describe what happens to the **position** of the image as the object is moved past C.

....

Mirrors

Q5 Julie is holding a small concave mirror in front of her in order to do her lipstick. The focal length of the mirror is 3 m. Tick **true** or **false** for each statement.

		True	False
a)	She sees a real image in the mirror.	☐	☐
b)	The distance from the vertex to the centre of curvature is 6 m.	☐	☐
c)	The mirror gives a magnified picture of her face.	☐	☐
d)	The mirror gives a wider field of view than a plane mirror.	☐	☐

Q6 A car's **rear-view mirror** often has a **convex** shape.

a) State one other practical use for a convex mirror.

....

b) What property of convex mirrors makes them useful as rear-view mirrors?

....

Q7 An incident ray that is parallel to the axis will be reflected from a convex mirror so that the reflected ray **seems** to come from the focal point.

a) Explain why the reflected ray can't have actually come from the focal point.

....

b) In the sentence below, **circle** the correct words from the choices given.

> An **extended** / **incident** ray that can be **extended** / **refracted** to pass through the focal point of a convex mirror will be reflected **along the normal** / **parallel to the axis**.

Q8 The diagram shows an object reflected in a convex mirror.

a) The diagram shows a ray from the top of the object striking the mirror. The dotted line shows the path the ray would have taken if the mirror wasn't there. On the diagram draw how the ray is reflected. Label the reflected ray as 'Ray 1'.

b) Draw the path of a ray coming from the top of the object parallel to the axis. Label the reflected ray as 'Ray 2'.

c) Sketch the position of the image on the diagram.

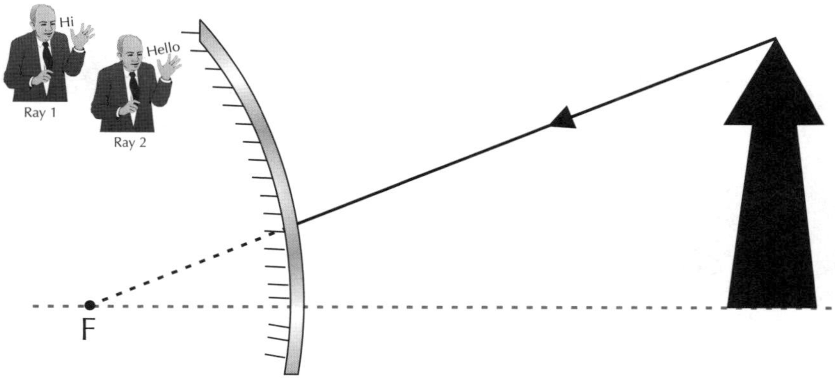

The top of the image is where Ray 1 and Ray 2 appear to come from.

Top Tips: When it comes to answering tricky questions, remember: the ray diagram is your friend. Don't panic — just draw in each ray carefully, one at a time, and Bob's your hamster.

Refractive Index and Snell's Law

Q1 Here is a diagram of a ray of light entering a material with **refractive index n.**

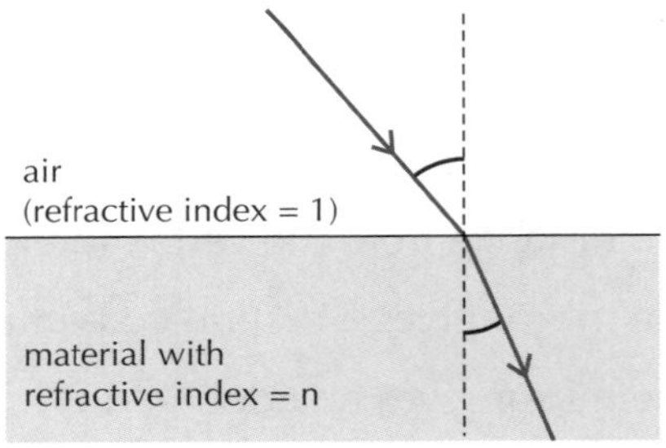

a) Label the following parts of the diagram:

Incident ray **Normal line** **Refracted ray**

Angle of incidence, i **Angle of refraction, r**

b) Snell's law relates the refractive index, **n** to the two angles **i** and **r**. Write down Snell's law.

....

Q2 A light ray was shone from air into some water. The ray had an **angle of incidence** of **30°** and an **angle of refraction** of **22°**. Use this data to calculate the **refractive index** of water.

....

....

....

Q3 A student was investigating the refractive index of a transparent material. She shone yellow light at various **angles of incidence (i)** and measured the **angles of refraction (r)**. She then filled in the table below:

i	r	sin i	sin r
10.0°	8.3°		
20.0°	16.4°		
30.0°	24.8°		
40.0°	32.3°		
50.0°	39.8°		
60.0°	46.2°		

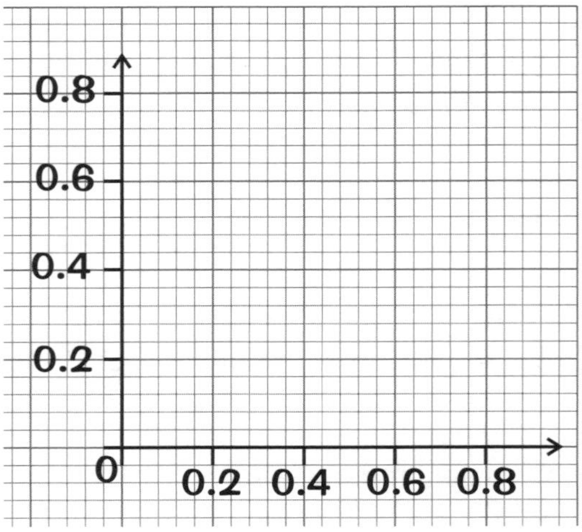

a) **Complete** the table and then draw a graph of **sin r** on the **y-axis** against **sin i** on the **x-axis**.

b) Explain why the **gradient** of the graph = **1/n**, where n is the refractive index of the material.

....

....

c) Use your graph to calculate the refractive index of the material for yellow light.

....

Refractive Index and Snell's Law

Q4 The diagram shows **white light** undergoing dispersion when it refracts from **air** into **glass**.

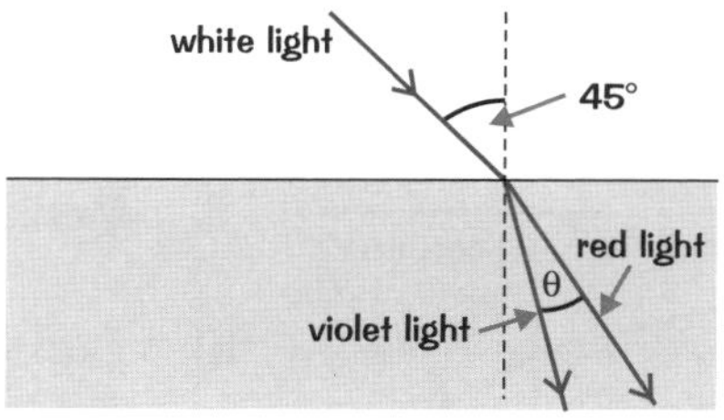

a) The refractive index in glass for red light is 1.514.
Calculate the **angle of refraction** for red light.

....

....

b) The refractive index in glass for violet light is 1.528.
What does this tell you about the **speed** of **violet** light in glass compared to **red** light?

....

c) Calculate the angle θ shown in the diagram.

....

....

Q5 Light passes through the acrylic bottom of a boat into the water below.
For blue light, the refractive index of **acrylic** is **1.498** (to 4 significant figures) and the refractive index of **water** is **1.337** (to 4 significant figures).

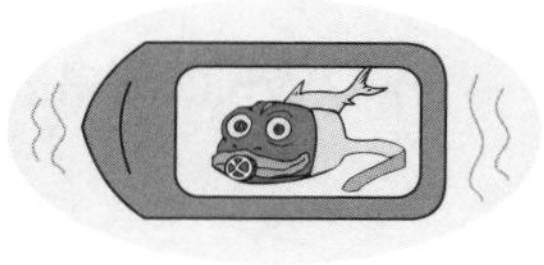

a) **i)** What happens to the **speed** of the light as it passes into the water?

....

ii) Complete this sentence by underlining the correct option.

The angle of refraction is greater than / less than the angle of incidence.

b) If the angle of incidence were equal to the critical angle, what would the **angle** of **refraction** be?

....

c) What happens to light which enters the water at an angle **greater** than the critical angle?

....

d) Calculate the **critical angle** for the **acrylic to water** boundary for blue light, to the nearest degree.

You'll need the equation with sin C in it.

....

....

....

....

Lenses

Q1 The diagram shows a ray of light passing across the **boundary** between two media.

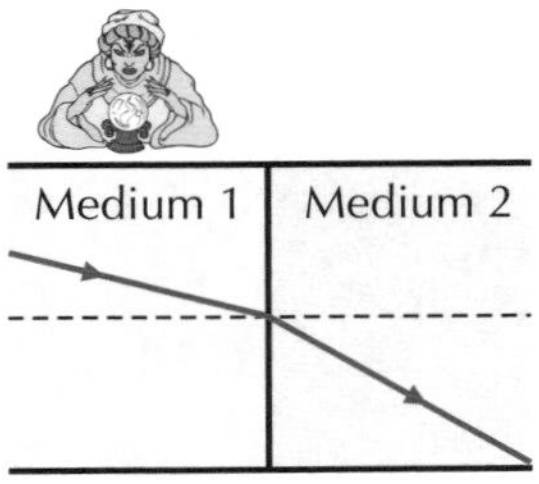

a) Which of Medium 1 and Medium 2 is air and which is glass?

Medium 1 is .... **Medium 2 is** ....

b) Explain your answer to a). ....

....

Q2 Benedict shines a beam of light at an angle through three glass prisms.

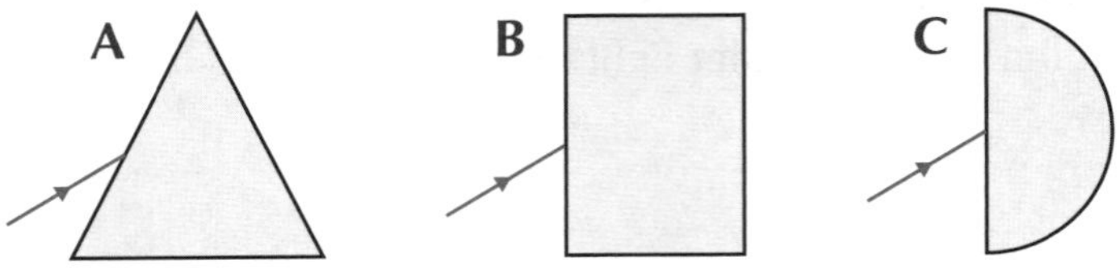

Sketch in the <u>normal</u> to each boundary first (Prism C's a bit tricky).

a) For each prism sketch the path the beam takes as it passes through and out the other side.

b) A beam of **white light** is sent into each of the prisms.
What would you see happening to the white light as it leaves Prism A?

....

c) What would you see as white light left Prism B? Explain your answer.

....

....

d) Which of these colours of light is refracted the **least**? Circle the correct answer.

violet green blue red orange

Q3 Lenses can be either **converging** or **diverging**.

a) Which type of lens has a virtual focus? ....

b) In the following sentences the words **parallel**, **converging**, **focal point** and **incident** have been replaced by the letters **W**, **X**, **Y**, **Z**. Write down which words are represented by **W**, **X**, **Y** and **Z**.

*An **W** ray passing through the centre of a **X** lens from any angle carries on in the same direction.*

*A **X** lens causes all **W** rays **Y** to the axis to meet at the **Z**.*

*A **X** lens causes all **W** rays passing through the **Z** to emerge **Y** to the axis.*

W .... **X** .... **Y** .... **Z** ....

c) Which of the following incident rays do not have their direction changed by either type of lens?
Tick any boxes which apply.

- ☐ Any ray parallel to the axis
- ☐ Any ray passing through the centre of the lens
- ☐ Any ray passing along the axis
- ☐ Any ray passing through the focal point

Lenses

Q4 The table below gives information about the images formed by a **converging lens** when the object is at different positions, where F is the focal point of the lens.

Distance from lens to object	Distance from lens to image	Type of image	Size of image
Greater than 2F	Between 2F and F	Real, inverted	Smaller than object
Equal to 2F		Real, inverted	
Between 2F and F	Greater than 2F		
Less than F	Greater than 2F		Larger than object

a) Fill in the blanks in the table.

b) An object has a height of 1 cm. It stands on the axis of a converging lens, 5 cm away from it. The focal length of the lens (distance from the lens to the focal point) is 2.5 cm.

i) What size will the image be?

....

ii) Where will the image be formed, relative to the lens and the object?

....

Q5 An aubergine is placed 6.1 cm away from a converging lens with a focal length of **7 cm.**

a) Will the image formed by the lens be:

i) upright or inverted? ....

ii) on the same side of the lens or on the opposite side? ....

iii) real or virtual? ....

b) The aubergine is now placed at a distance *X* from the lens. The image is now bigger than the object and inverted. Which of the options below could be distance *X*? Circle your answer.

A 3.9 cm **B** 7.0 cm **C** 10.2 cm **D** 14.0 cm **E** 15.3 cm

Q6 The diagram below shows an object placed next to a diverging lens. The focal points are marked.

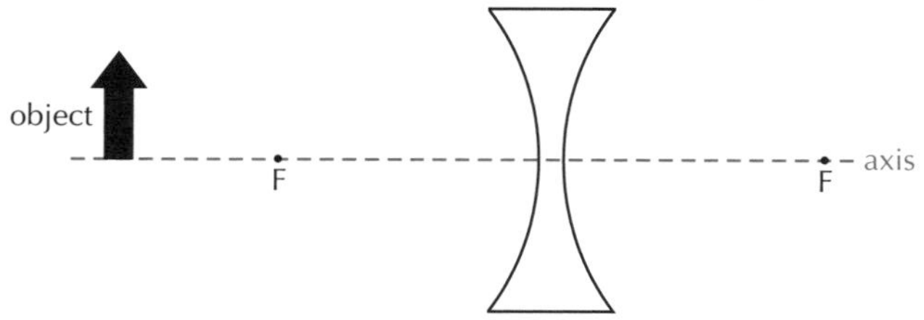

a) On the diagram, draw the path of a ray coming from the top of the object and travelling in the direction of the centre of the lens.

b) Draw the path of a ray coming from the top of the object and going towards the focal point on the far side of the lens.

c) Draw the image formed by the lens.

Uses — Magnification and Cameras

Q1 Magnifying glasses use convex lenses to produce images which are **larger** than the object.

a) What is the **furthest distance** the object can be from the lens when a convex lens is used as a magnifier?

....

b) Will the image be a **real** image or a **virtual** one? ....

c) What **test** could you do to check whether the image is real or virtual?

....

Q2 The magnification of a lens system can be worked out using the **heights** of the **object** and the **image**.

a) Write down the formula relating magnification, object height and image height.

....

b) A **1.5 cm** stamp was observed through a magnifying glass. The virtual image it produced was **6 cm** high. What was the magnification?

....

c) A camera was used to take the picture of a tree. If the magnification was **0.002** and the image of the tree was **2 cm** high, what was the **actual height** of the tree?

....

Q3 **Complete** the ray diagram and **take measurements** to find the magnification of this system.

Draw the diagram REALLY carefully.

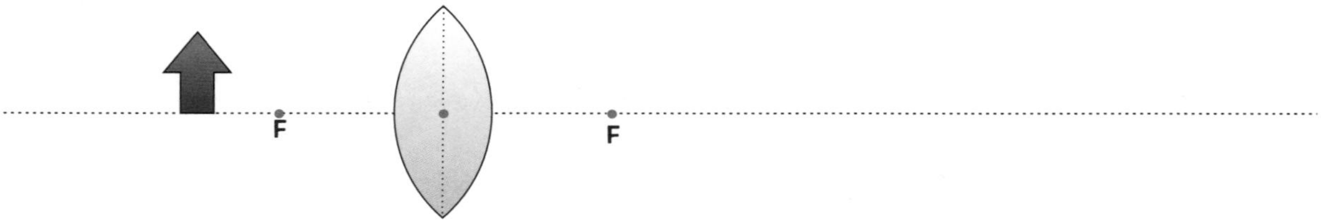

....

Uses — Magnification and Cameras

Q4 **Lenses** are used in **cameras.**

a) Delete the incorrect words in these statements about a camera being used to take a normal family photo.

The magnification is **less than 1 / exactly 1 / less than 1.**

The image is **real / virtual.**

The image is **upside down / the right way up.**

b) Here is a ray diagram for a camera taking a photo of a flower.

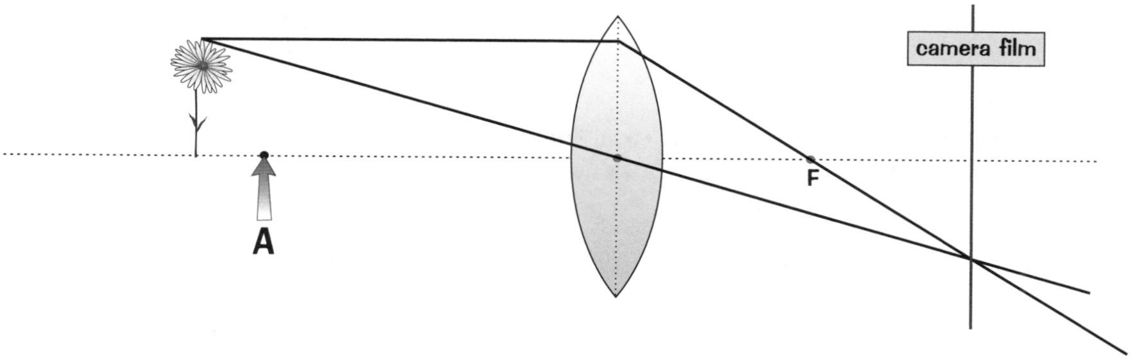

The flower is moved closer to the lens, to the point A in the diagram. Draw in a new ray diagram to show where the new image will be.

c) What would you have to do to the camera to keep the image focused on the film?

....

Q5 This question is about the uses of **lenses in film projectors.**

a) Delete the incorrect words in these statements about lenses in film projectors.

The magnification is **less than 1 / exactly 1 / more than 1.**

The image is **real / virtual.**

The image is **upside down / the right way up.**

b) **Which way up** must the **film** (the object) go in order to produce the correct image on the cinema screen?

....

c) A film projector was moved from one cinema to another cinema where the screen was **further away** from the projector. How should the distance between the **film** and the **lens** be changed in order to focus the picture correctly on the cinema screen?

....

Interference of Waves

Q1 The diagrams below each show **displacement–time graphs** of two waves that are **overlapping**.

On each set of empty axes, draw what the graph of the **combined wave** would look like.
Also decide whether the interference is **constructive** or **destructive** — circle the correct answer.

a)

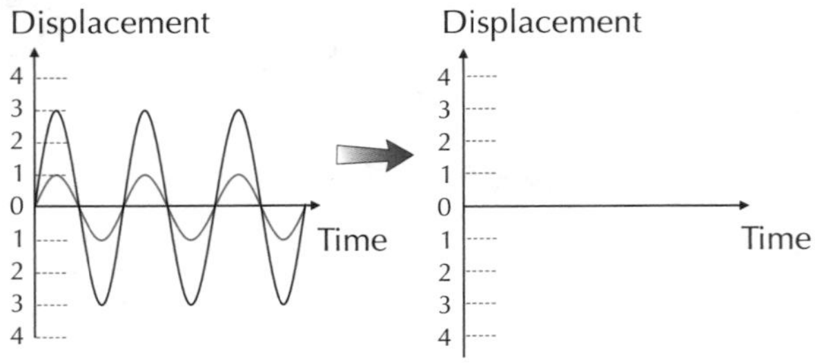

This is **constructive** / **destructive** interference.

b)

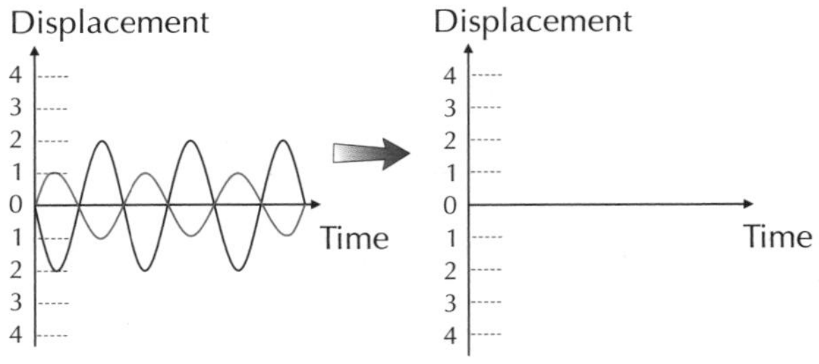

This is **constructive** / **destructive** interference.

Q2 Caleb was in a science lesson listening to a single musical note that his teacher was playing through a loudspeaker. To his surprise, when his teacher connected up **another speaker**, the sound got **quieter** rather than **louder**.

a) **Explain** what was happening to the two sound waves at the place where Caleb was sitting.

b) Caleb then got up and walked around the lab. Describe what he might have heard as he walked around.

Q3 **Laser light** was shone onto a screen through two very **thin slits** that were close together.

a) Describe what you would see on the screen.

b) The slits are much **closer together** than the loudspeakers in Q2. Why is this?

c) Which of these situations would give **destructive** interference? Circle the correct letter.

A A path difference of an odd number of whole wavelengths

B A path difference of an odd number of half wavelengths

C A path difference of an even number of half wavelengths.

Diffraction Patterns and Polarisation

Q1 Circle **true** or **false** for each of the statements below.

a) Normal light waves are transverse waves vibrating in a mixture of directions. True / False

b) Longitudinal waves can be plane polarised. True / False

c) Plane polarised waves only vibrate in one direction. True / False

d) Diffraction patterns are only formed by plane polarised light. True / False

Q2 A **laser** beam was projected onto a screen through a pair of **Polaroid sunglasses**. When the glasses were **rotated** 42°, they blocked the light completely.

a) What does this tell you about laser light?

....

b) The experiment is repeated using a **torch** instead of a laser. What would you expect to see now when the sunglasses were rotated 42°?

....

c) The torch beam is then reflected off a **glass plate** on the bench as shown in the diagram.

What happens now when the sunglasses are rotated?

....

....

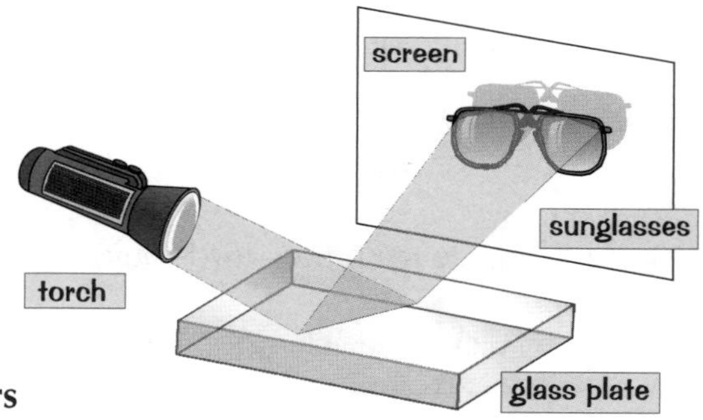

d) Explain why Polaroid sunglasses are useful for **car drivers** on a sunny day when the roads are wet.

....

....

Q3 A **laser** beam was shone towards a screen through a **small circular hole**. The pattern shown was seen on the screen. Explain how this pattern is formed.

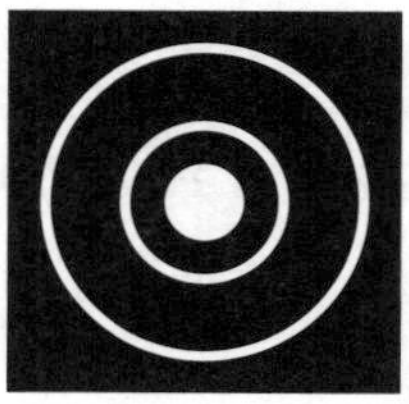

....

....

....

Top Tips: The light does what now? Remember that only transverse waves can be plane polarised and that it's soooo useful. I mean, where would we be without our shades to look cool?

Sound Waves

Q1 Sound waves are caused by **vibrations**.

Put the following sentences in the correct order to describe how the sound of a drumbeat is made and reaches our ears.

A The vibration of the drum sets the air molecules next to it vibrating too.

B We hear the sound when the vibrations in the air set our eardrums vibrating at the same frequency.

C When someone beats a drum, the skin on top of the drum vibrates.

D A series of compressions and decompressions travel outwards through the air (or other medium) as a longitudinal wave.

Correct order: .... , ... , ... , ...

Q2 This table shows the speed of sound in water, wood and air at room temperature.

Medium	Speed of sound (m/s)
wood	4120
water	1497
air	344

a) In which of the three media does sound travel most slowly? ....

b) Based on the data, does sound travel faster through a liquid or a solid? ....

Q3 Choose from the words below to fill in the spaces in the passage.

high wavelength amplitude low refract frequency quiet vibrate

A sound wave makes air molecules .... If there are many vibrations per second the frequency or pitch of the sound is .... If there are only a few vibrations per second the pitch of the sound is .... If the air molecules vibrate with a large .... the sound is loud. If each air molecule vibrates over a small distance then the sound is ....

Q4 Humans can't hear sounds outside the frequency range 20 Hz to 20 000 Hz.

a) What is the frequency of a sound wave that has 30 compressions in one second?

....

b) Put the following frequencies in order, from the lowest frequency to the highest.

3 MHz, 8 kHz, 630 Hz, 400 kHz, 5 Hz, 21 kHz

....

Sound Waves

Q5 Mina sings in her school choir. She practises both in her bedroom and in an empty practice room at school. She hears a difference in the sound of her voice, caused by a difference in echo.

a) What is an echo?

....

b) Why were there lots of echoes in the unfurnished practice room but not in her bedroom at home?

....

Q6 In an experiment, a ringing alarm clock is placed in a glass bell jar. Air is sucked out of the jar by a vacuum pump.

a) What happens to the sound and why?

....

....

b) Why does the experiment work better if the alarm clock is placed on top of a block of foam?

....

Q7 This CRO trace shows the waveform for a clear, pure note.

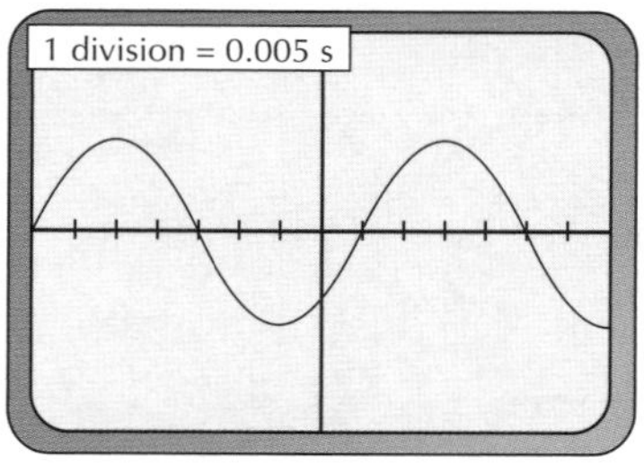

a) What is the shape of this type of wave called?

....

b) How long does one full vibration take?

....

c) What is the frequency of the wave in hertz?

1 Hz is one vibration per second.

....

d) On the same diagram, draw a waveform for a sound that has the same frequency but is louder.

Q8 Different types of instrument, e.g. a piano and a trumpet, will always sound different, even if they're producing notes of the same pitch and loudness.

How is the quality of a note shown on its oscilloscope trace?

....

Ultrasound

Q1 a) What is ultrasound?

....

b) How can ultrasound of a particular frequency be generated?

....

....

Q2 Yesterday Sean used an oscilloscope to study the frequency and amplitude of ordinary sound waves. Today he needs to use the same piece of equipment to study ultrasound.

What adjustment does Sean need to make to the oscilloscope?

....

....

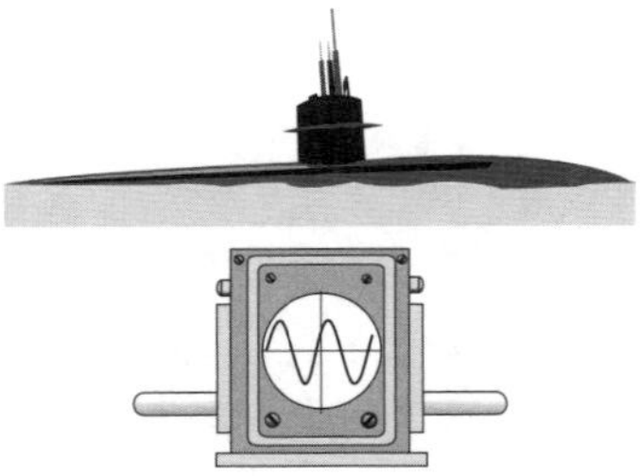

Sean used an oscilloscope to study the enemy's waves.

Q3 A building engineer suspects that there is a crack in a ceiling girder. He uses an ultrasonic scanner to send a beam of ultrasound into the girder.

a) If a crack is present, describe the two boundaries that the ultrasound wave will encounter.

....

....

b) The diagram shows a beam of ultrasound striking the first of the two boundaries. Sketch what happens to the beam next.

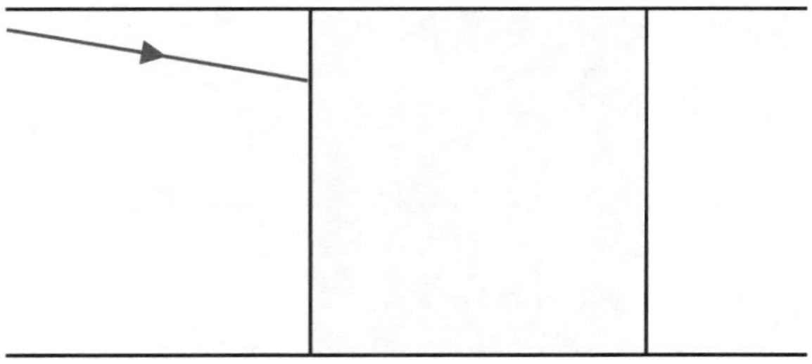

c) Why is it important to know the speed of sound in a medium between two boundaries in order to discover how far apart the two boundaries are?

....

....

Top Tips: Ultrasound can be pretty useful. From reflections of ultrasound we can see how a foetus is developing, and bats can tell where they're going. Without it, there'd be a lot of lost bats.

Uses of Ultrasound

Q1 Ultrasound is used to make prenatal scans of a foetus.

a) For prenatal scanning, why is it better to use ultrasound than X-rays?

b) Use the key words below to write a brief explanation of how a prenatal scan works.

reflected | monitor | processed | foetus | uterus

boundary | image | amniotic fluid | ultrasound

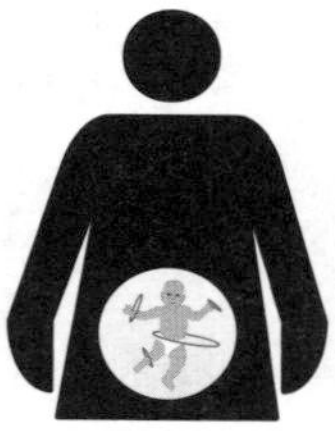

c) Give another medical use of ultrasound.

Q2 A pulse of ultrasound is used to find the size of a large crack under the ground, through which water is flowing. Inside the crack, the ultrasound has a frequency of 28 kHz and a wavelength of 5 cm. A CRO trace shows the two reflected pulses are 130 μs apart.

a) Calculate the speed of the ultrasound within the crack.

Convert everything to SI units first.

b) Calculate the width of the crack, showing your workings.

Top Tips: The really important thing to remember when doing echo questions is that the ultrasound has to travel to the boundary and back, so it's travelled double the distance.

Potential Dividers

Q1 Complete the sentences by circling the correct word or words.

a) A potential divider consists of a **single resistor** / **pair of resistors**.

b) The higher the value of a resistor the **bigger** / **smaller** the voltage drop across it.

Q2 Tick the boxes to show whether the following statements are **true** or **false**.

	True	False
a) The voltage at the point between the resistors is the output of the potential divider.	☐	☐
b) If the resistors are of equal value then the output voltage will be 50% of the total voltage.	☐	☐
c) To vary the output, both the resistors must be variable resistors.	☐	☐

Q3 The diagram shows a potential divider consisting of resistors R_1 and R_2.

a) Complete the statements below about how the output voltage can be **varied**.

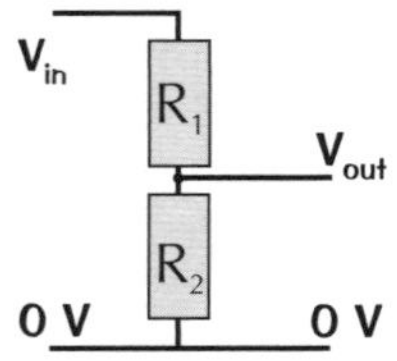

i) If the output voltage is too low you could **increase** it by .... the resistance of resistor $\mathbf{R_1}$.

ii) If the output voltage is too high you could **decrease** it by .... the resistance of resistor ....

b) Complete the following passage by underlining the correct words.

> If resistor R_1 was replaced with a thermistor, the output voltage would be highest when it was **hot** / **cold**. This is because a thermistor's resistance **increases** / **decreases** with rising temperature.

Q4 The diagram shows a potential divider. Calculate the **output voltage** V_{out} for each of the following sets of values for R_1 and R_2.

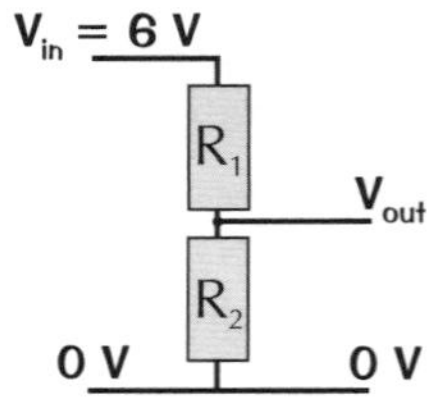

a) $R_1 = R_2 = 10\ \Omega$. ....

....

b) $R_1 = 20\ \Omega$. $R_2 = 10\ \Omega$. ....

....

Q5 Two resistors, R_1 and R_2, make up a potential divider. The total **input voltage** is **6 V**. The graph shows how the **output voltage** changes as R_1 is changed and R_2 is kept constant.

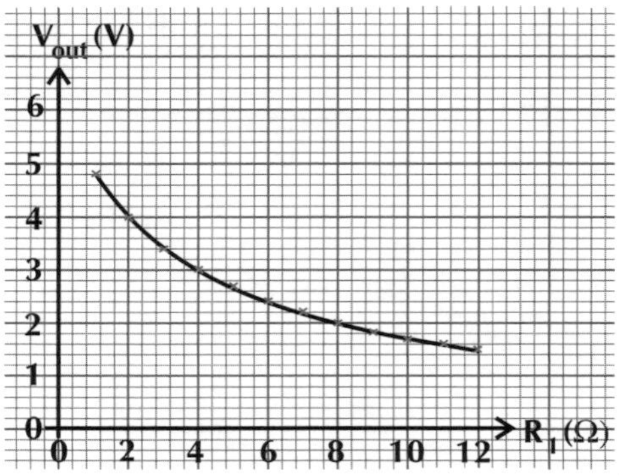

a) What value of R_1 gives an output voltage of **2.2 V**?

....

b) What value of R_1 gives an output voltage of **6.0 V**?

....

c) Use the graph to find the value of $\mathbf{R_2}$.

....

Diodes and Rectification

Q1 Match up each keyword with the correct description.

Semiconductor	has empty spaces called 'holes' where electrons are missing
n-type semiconductor	conducts electricity but not as well as a conductor
p-type semiconductor	allows a current to flow in one direction only
Diode	has extra free electrons

Q2 a) Tick the boxes to show whether the following statements are **true** or **false**.

	True	False
i) The element silicon is a semiconductor.	☐	☐
ii) Semiconductors have low resistance in one direction and high resistance in the other.	☐	☐
iii) n-type semiconductors contain impurities but p-type semiconductors do not.	☐	☐
iv) 'Holes' effectively have a positive charge.	☐	☐
v) You need both p- and n-type semiconductors in a diode.	☐	☐

b) Write down correct versions of the false statements.

....

....

....

....

....

Q3 Diodes can be used to **rectify** AC current.

a) i) What does 'rectification' mean?

....

ii) Why is it sometimes necessary to rectify an AC current?

....

b) Which is the simpler method — half-wave rectification or full-wave rectification?

....

c) How many diodes are required for full-wave rectification?

....

Diodes and Rectification

Q4 Why are impurities deliberately put into semiconductors?

....

Q5 Describe what happens to the 'holes' and electrons at the p-n junction in a diode when there is **no potential difference** across the diode.

....

....

Q6 Explain, in terms of the movement of electrons, why a current flows in circuit A but not in circuit B.

Circuit A

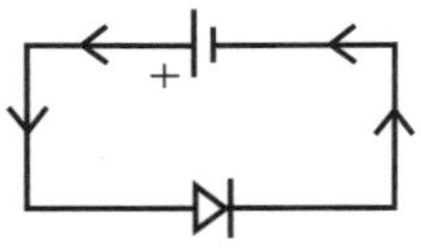

Circuit B

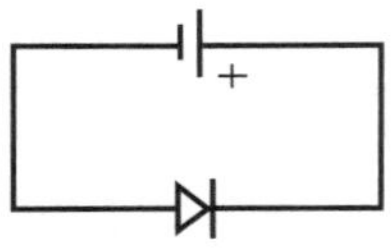

For this one, a sketched diagram on a bit of scrap paper might help. Or you could think about where the electrons 'want' to go.

....

....

....

....

Q7 A single diode in series with an AC supply gives **half-wave rectification**.

a) Complete the diagram below to show the output voltage over time from the circuit shown.

HALF-WAVE RECTIFICATION

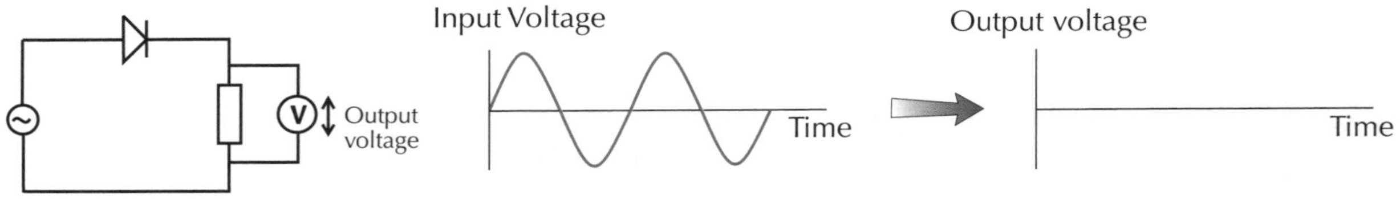

b) The diagram shows a bridge circuit which could be used to give **full-wave rectification**, but the diodes are missing.

Complete the diagram to show the position of the diodes in the circuit.

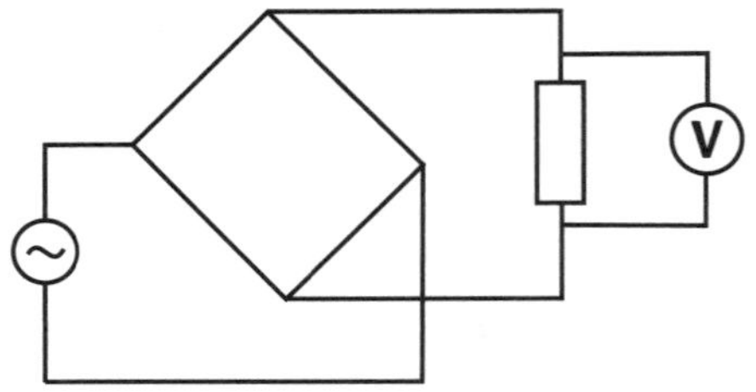

Top Tips: Yes, the circuit for Q7 b) is a bit of a pig. It's something that could come up in the exam, though, so **be prepared** to sketch it out. If you can explain how it works, so much the better. It's well worth learning how p-type and n-type semiconductors make a diode work, too.

Capacitors

Q1 Describe how to **fully charge** a capacitor.

Q2 a) Indicate whether the following statements are **true** or **false**.

	True	False
i) The higher the voltage of the power supply, the more charge a capacitor can store.	☐	☐
ii) A capacitor can be used to store electric current.	☐	☐

b) Write correct versions of any false statements.

Q3 Capacitors are used in **smoothing circuits** like the one shown.

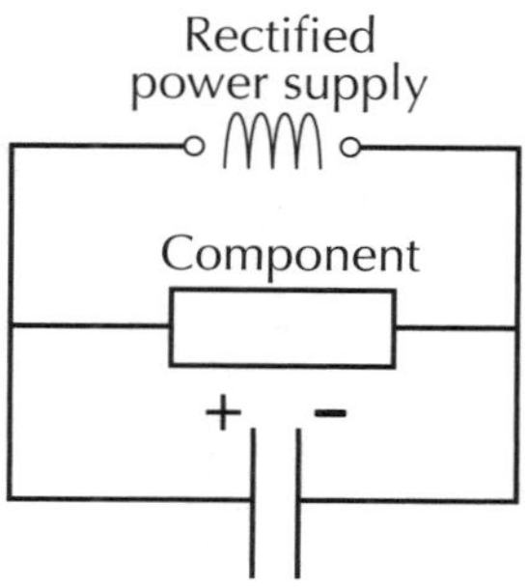

a) Why is it often necessary to smooth a rectified AC voltage?

b) Where does current flow when the input voltage is **high**?

c) Where does current flow when the input voltage is **low**?

d) Explain why the current through the component stays more or less steady.

Q4 The diagram shows a **time delay** circuit. When the power supply to the circuit is switched on it takes a while for the output voltage, V_{out}, to rise.

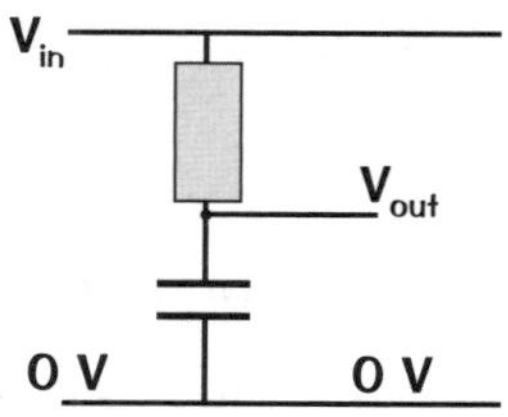

The sentences below explain how the time delay circuit works. Complete them by circling the correct words or phrases.

1. Initially the capacitor **is fully charged** / **has no charge stored**, so the voltage across it is **large** / **small** and the output voltage is **large** / **small**.
2. Charge flows into the capacitor so the voltage across it gradually **increases** / **decreases** and the voltage across the resistor **increases** / **decreases**.
3. As this happens the output voltage gradually **rises** / **falls**.

Logic Gates

Q1 Fill in the gaps in the following sentences about logic gates.

a) An electronic system in which the only possible values are **on** and **off** is described as a .... system.

b) A **NOT** gate is sometimes called an ....

Q2 Write the **correct component name** under each symbol.

a)

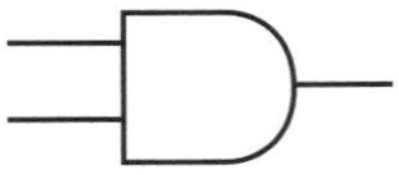

....

b)

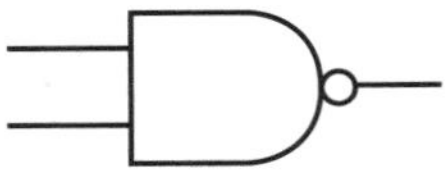

....

c)

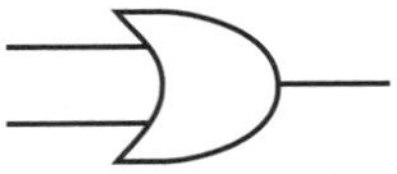

....

d)

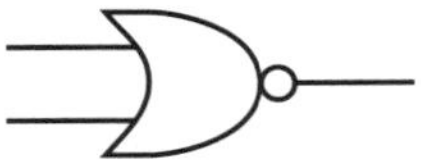

....

e)

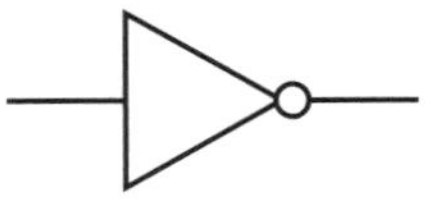

....

Q3 What kind of logic gate would give each of the truth tables below? Write the correct title and draw the correct symbol under each truth table.

A	B	Output
0	0	1
0	1	0
1	0	0
1	1	0

....

A	B	Output
0	0	0
0	1	0
1	0	0
1	1	1

....

A	B	Output
0	0	1
0	1	1
1	0	1
1	1	0

....

in	out
0	1
1	0

....

Q4 Peter draws a truth table for a **NAND** gate. He makes mistakes.

a) Correct his mistakes in the table.

b) What combination of two gates would be the same as a NAND gate?

.... then ....

A	B	Output
0	0	0
0	1	1
1	0	1
1	1	1

Q5 For each of the following descriptions write down the **name** of the **logic gate** which fits.

a) Output is 0 unless all inputs are 0. ....

b) Output is 1 if input is 0. ....

c) The only time output is 1 is when both inputs are 1. ....

d) Output is 1 unless both inputs are 1. ....

Using Logic Gates

Q1 This diagram shows a **logic circuit.**

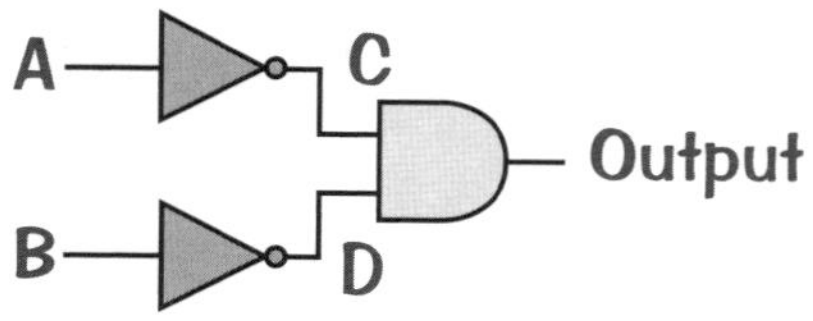

A	B	C	D	Output
0	0			
1	0			
0	1			
1	1			

Marie thinks that this logic circuit might be the same as a **NOR** gate. She plans a truth table to prove it:

a) Finish the truth table by inserting all the missing values.

b) Was Marie's idea correct — is this circuit the same as a NOR gate? ....

Q2 Mr Green's shop has **three doors.** He wants a bell to ring if **any** door opens.

He designs the following logic circuit.

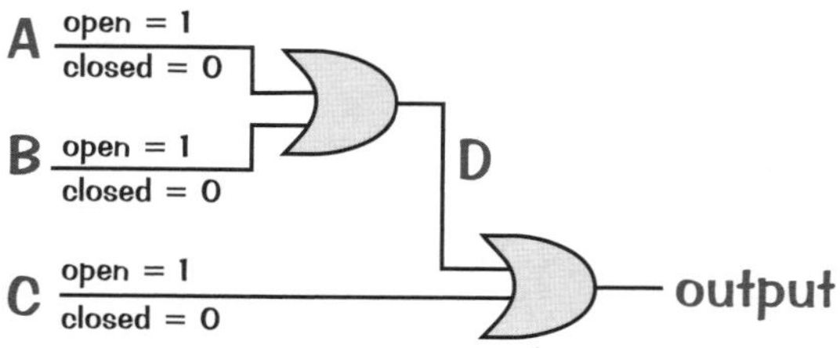

A	B	C	D	Output
0	0	0		
0	0	1		
0	1	0		
0	1	1		
1	0	0		
1	0	1		
1	1	0		
1	1	1		

a) Complete the truth table for the logic circuit.

b) Will the bell ring when **any one** door is opened? ....

c) Will the bell ring if **two or more** doors are opened? ....

Q3 This diagram shows a **NOR** latch circuit connected to a warning light.

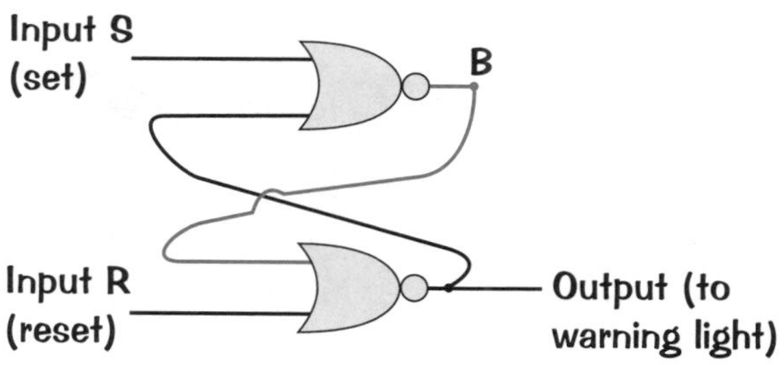

a) Initially, both inputs are 0 and the light is off.

i) **Input S** changes to **1**. Explain what happens.

....

....

....

ii) Input S changes back to **0** again. What happens now? Explain your answer.

....

....

b) If the main output is **1**, explain how it can be **reset** (to **0**). ....

....

LEDs and Relays in Logic Circuits

Q1 Indicate whether the following statements are **true** or **false**.

		True	False
a)	Current can only flow one way through an LED.	☐	☐
b)	LEDs need a large current to work.	☐	☐
c)	An LED uses very little power.	☐	☐

Q2 LEDs can be used to show the output of a **logic gate**.

a) Give **two** reasons why LEDs rather than ordinary lamp bulbs are used in logic circuits.

....

....

b) Why is an LED usually connected in series with a resistor?

....

Q3 Logic gates are often used to switch devices on and off.

a) Explain why logic gates can't be used to switch devices on and off in **high current** circuits.

....

b) Suggest how a logic circuit could be used to switch on a starter motor, even though the starter motor needs a high current.

....

....

Q4 A relay uses an **electromagnet** to connect two circuits.

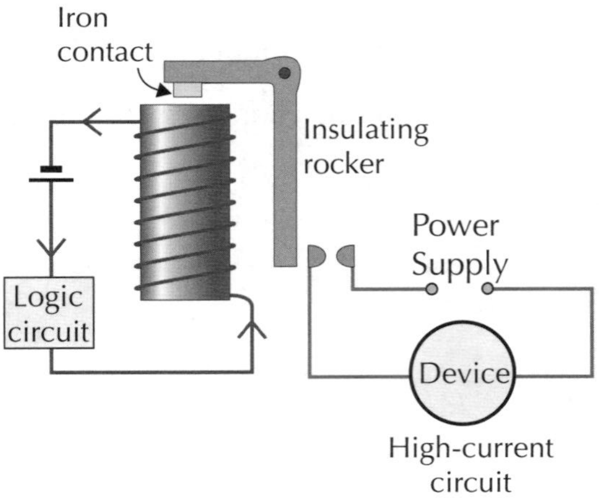

a) Explain how the logic circuit shown in the diagram can switch the high-current circuit on and off.

....

....

....

....

....

b) Describe a safety benefit of using a relay to switch on or off a device which requires a large current.

....

Kinetic Theory and Temperature in Gases

Q1 Complete the following paragraph using words from the box below.

0 °C	ice	0 K	100 °C	–273 °C	absolute	water

The Celsius temperature scale has two fixed points. One is the melting point of .... at .... The other is the boiling point of .... at .... The fixed point on the Kelvin temperature scale is at the lowest temperature possible — called .... zero. This is given a value of .... and it is equivalent to a temperature on the Celsius scale of about ....

Q2 Complete the following sentences by choosing the correct word or symbol from each pair.

a) At 0 **°C** / **K** the internal energy of any substance is at its lowest possible value.

b) When a gas is heated, the particles in it move **faster** / **more slowly**.

c) The average **kinetic** / **potential** energy of particles in a gas is **equal** / **proportional** to the temperature of the gas in kelvin.

Q3 Convert the following temperatures to **kelvin** (K).

a) 3 °C .... **b)** 210 °C ....

c) –45 °C .... **d)** 0 °C ....

Q4 Convert the following temperatures to **°C**.

a) 0 K .... **b)** 300 K ....

c) 640 K .... **d)** 30 K ....

Q5 The kinetic energy of particles depends on their **mass** and their **velocity**.

a) What is the formula for the kinetic energy of a particle of mass **m** travelling at velocity **v**?

....

b) The temperature of a gas is increased from 277 °C to 827 °C. At 277 °C the mean kinetic energy of the gas is 1.14×10^{20} joules. What is it at 827 °C?

....

....

Always start a kinetic theory question involving temperature by converting degrees Celsius to kelvin.

c) Explain why it takes longer for the smell of air freshener to spread through a room on a cold day than on a hot day.

....

Kinetic Theory and Pressure in Gases

Q1 **Kinetic theory** can be used to explain the behaviour and properties of gases.

a) What does kinetic theory say that a gas consists of? Choose **two** options from A to E below.

A stationary particles B very small particles C a rigid mesh of particles

D mostly empty space E fluctuations in electric and magnetic fields

b) Explain how the impact of gas molecules on the sides of a container relates to the pressure of a gas.

....

....

Q2 The apparatus shown in the diagram can be used to show how **pressure** changes with **temperature** for a gas.

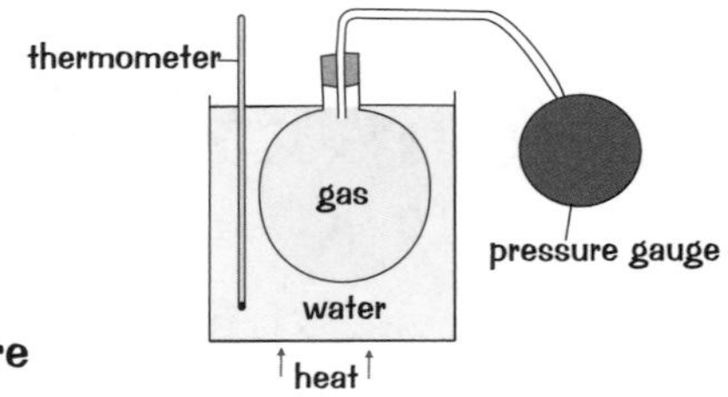

a) What variable is kept constant by having the gas in a rigid, sealed container? Circle the correct letter.

A Pressure B Volume C Temperature

b) On the graph below, point A shows the pressure and temperature of the gas when an experiment began. Point B is the point at which the gas could not be heated any more with this apparatus. Explain why B occurs at a temperature of 100 °C.

....

....

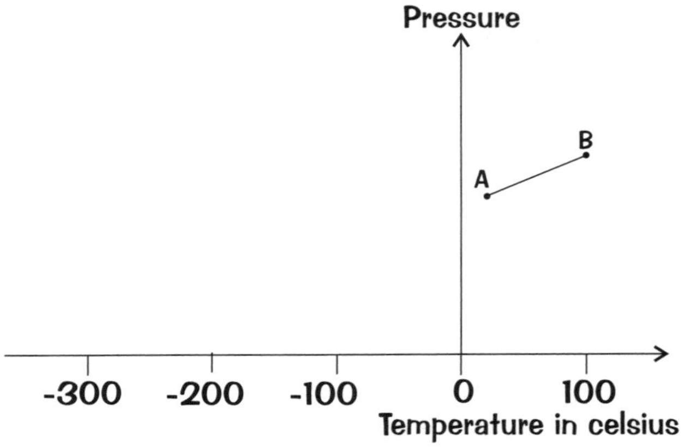

c) On the graph, continue the line to show how an ideal gas would behave if it was **cooled** to absolute zero.

d) At what temperature in celsius would the pressure be **zero**?

....

Q3 A bubble of carbon dioxide leaves a plant at the bottom of a lake. Initially it has a volume of **5 cm^3** and is at a pressure of **6 atm**. The temperature at the bottom of the lake is **4 °C**. The bubble rises and just before it reaches the surface it is at a pressure of **1 atm** and a temperature of **20 °C**.

a) Give two reasons why the volume of the bubble will **increase** as it rises.

1. ....

2. ....

b) Calculate the **volume** of the bubble just before it reaches the surface.

Don't forget to convert temperatures to kelvin.

....

....

Particles in Atoms

Q1 Alpha, beta and gamma are all types of ionising radiation, but they have quite different properties.

a) Rate the different types of radiation according to their penetrating power.

1 = high penetrating power
2 = moderate penetrating power
3 = low penetrating power

alpha ☐ beta ☐ gamma ☐

b) How does the **penetrating power** of each type of radiation compare to its **ionising power**?

....

c) Give an example of a material that can stop:

i) **alpha** radiation .... **ii)** **beta** radiation ....

Q2 Complete the following sentences about **radioactive decay**.

a) During β^- decay a .... becomes a .... The atomic number increases by 1 and the mass number ....

b) During β^+ decay a .... becomes a .... The atomic number .... and the mass number stays the same.

c) α, β^+ and β^- decay all result in the formation of a different ...., which is shown by the change in .... number.

Q3 Neutrons are found in the nuclei of atoms and can also be emitted as a form of radiation. Underline the correct words from the options given.

a) Neutron radiation is **more** / **less** penetrating than alpha or beta radiation.

b) Neutrons do not have electric **charge** / **power** so they do not directly **absorb** / **ionise** material they pass through.

c) Absorbing a neutron can make a nucleus **ionised** / **radioactive**.

Q4 The equation shows an isotope of carbon undergoing radioactive decay.

$$^{14}_{6}C \rightarrow X + ^{0}_{+1}e$$

a) What type of radioactive decay is this?

....

b) Give the **nucleon number** and **atomic number** of element X.

nucleon number: .... atomic number: ....

c) People take precautions against cell damage from ionisation by most types of radiation.
Why is it not necessary to take particular precautions against this type of radiation?

....

Particles in Atoms

Q5 The graph on the right shows the number of neutrons (N) against the number of protons (Z) for **stable isotopes**.

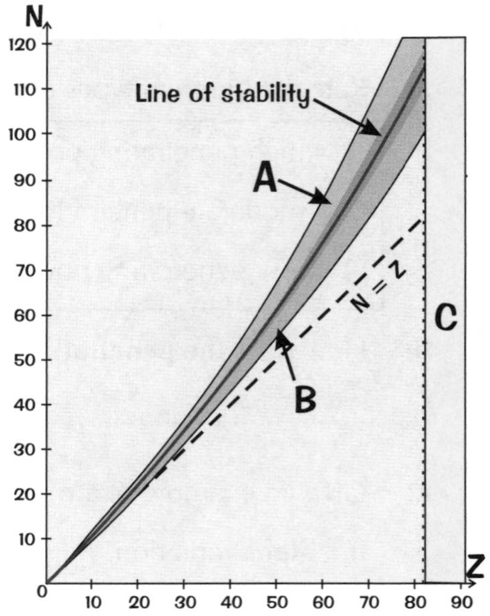

a) What are **isotopes** of an element?

....

....

b) Are isotopes in region A stable or unstable?
Circle your answer.

stable unstable

c) Are isotopes in region A neutron-rich or proton-rich?

neutron-rich proton-rich

d) Suggest a reason why isotopes in region B are **unstable**.

....

e) In order to achieve stability, what type of decay will isotopes in **region B** undergo?

....

f) What type of particle will isotopes in **region C** emit? ....

Q6 **Alpha particles** are strongly ionising.

a) What kinds of atom undergo alpha decay?

....

b) Complete this nuclear equation.

$$^{224}_{88}Ra \rightarrow {}^{\square}_{\square}Rn + {}^{\square}_{\square}\text{alpha}$$

c) After alpha (or beta) decay, a nucleus often has too much energy. How does it lose this energy?

....

Q7 Shielding made of **concrete** can be used as protection against neutron radiation.

a) What type of nuclei are best for absorbing neutron radiation? ....

b) Concrete shielding alone is not enough to prevent harmful effects from neutron radiation. Explain why.

....

....

Fundamental and Other Particles

Q1 Many particles can be split into even smaller particles.

a) What is a **fundamental particle**?

....

b) Circle the fundamental particles in the box below.

Proton	Electron	Neutron	Monkey	Positron	Alpha particle

c) Can new fundamental particles ever be created? If so, how?

....

Q2 Tick the statements that are **true**.

A Quarks are made up of protons and neutrons. ☐

B The relative mass of a quark is 1/3. ☐

C All quarks have the same charge. ☐

D There are 2 quarks in a proton. ☐

E There are 2 types of quark in a neutron. ☐

Q3 Match the **particles** on the left with the correct description of their **properties**.

- Electron
- Down-quark
- Proton
- Neutron
- Positron
- Up-quark

- relative mass 1/3, relative charge 2/3
- relative mass 1, charge +1
- fundamental particle, charge –1
- relative charge –1/3
- made up of two down-quarks and one up-quark
- fundamental particle, charge +1

Q4 The number of protons and neutrons in a nucleus can make it **unstable**. Complete the following passage by choosing from the words in blue.

proton   beta-minus decay   neutron   electron   beta-plus decay

To become more stable, the nucleus can convert a neutron into a(n) .... To keep the overall charge zero, the nucleus must then emit a(n) .... This process is called ....

Fundamental and Other Particles

Q5 Scientists at **CERN** carry out experiments involving smashing particles together at high speed.

a) Fill in the **gaps** in this passage.

In an experiment, two protons are .... to very high speeds and made to collide. The collision releases a large amount of ....
Some of this .... can be turned into mass which is equal parts .... and anti.....................................

b) Antimatter is made up of antiparticles.

i) Give one **similarity** between a particle and its antiparticle. ....

ii) Give one **difference** between a particle and its antiparticle. ....

iii) Name the antiparticle of the electron. ....

c) The **antiproton** is the antiparticle of the proton. Is the antiproton a fundamental particle? Explain your answer.

....

d) What is the relative **charge** on an antiproton? ....

Q6 The charges on **protons** and **neutrons** are determined by the **quarks** that form them.

a) Make simple sketch diagrams of a **proton** and a **neutron**, showing the number and type of quarks each contains.

Proton	Neutron

b) Complete the blanks in this sentence:

In beta-plus decay, a proton is converted to a ....
and a .... is emitted.

c) Describe β^+ decay in terms of what happens to the quarks in a proton.

....

Top Tips: Everything, everywhere is made of particles — make sure you know each type, its charge and relative mass. Learn which are fundamental, and how they go together to make the rest.

Electron Beams

Q1 The diagram shows an **electron gun**.

a) Use the following words to fill in the labels on the diagram. Words may be used more than once.

vacuum
heater
electrons
anode
deflecting
cathode

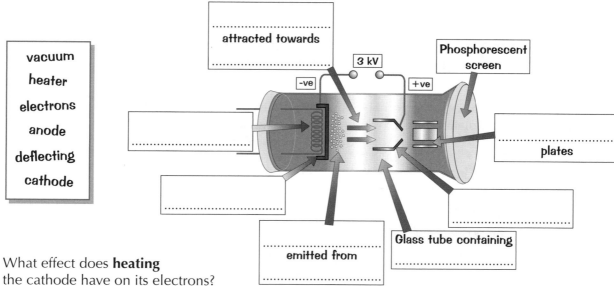

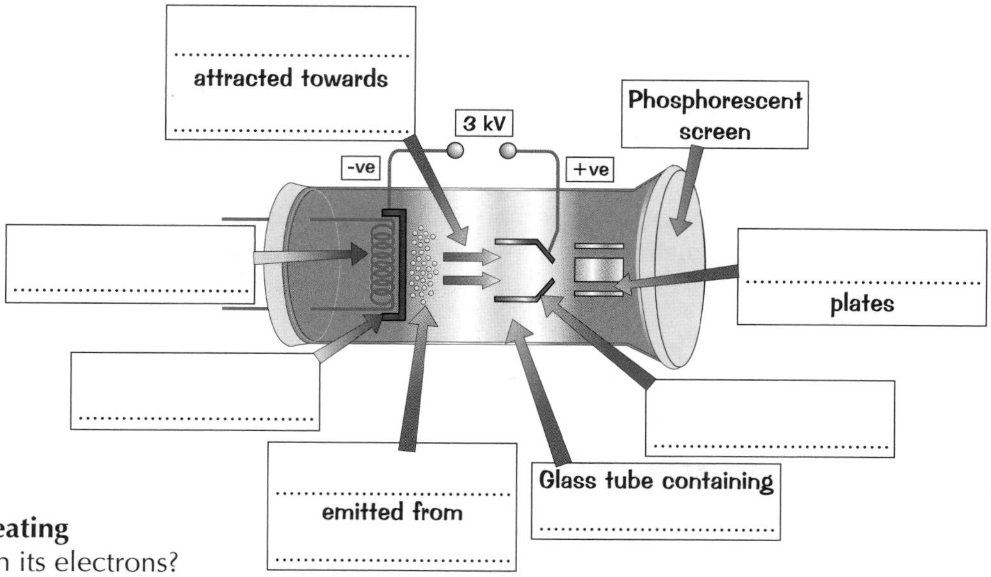

b) What effect does **heating** the cathode have on its electrons?

....

c) Which components in the electron gun use electric fields to make electrons change:

i) speed? ....

ii) direction? ....

d) What happens when an electron hits the phosphorescent screen?

....

Q2 A beam of electrons leaves an **electron gun**. The current carried by the beam is 4 mA.

a) What is current a measure of?

....

b) How many **coulombs** of charge pass a certain point in the beam per second?

....

c) How many **electrons** pass this point per second?

....

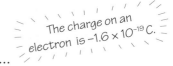

The charge on an electron is -1.6×10^{-19} C.

Q3 The electron beam in a cathode ray tube is deflected by the **electric field** between two pairs of charged metal plates. Circle the correct words from each pair to complete the following sentences.

a) The electron beam is **attracted to / repelled by** a positive charge and **attracted to / repelled by** a negative charge.

b) The **Y-plates / X-plates** deflect the beam up or down, while the **Y-plates / X-plates** deflect the beam left or right.

Electron Beams

Q4 The diagram below shows the screen of an **oscilloscope**. The position of the spot of light is controlled by charged metal plates that **deflect** the beam of electrons from the cathode ray tube.

The dot shows the position of the electron beam when a positive potential is connected to X1 and Y1, so X1 is more positive than X2 and Y1 is more positive than Y2.

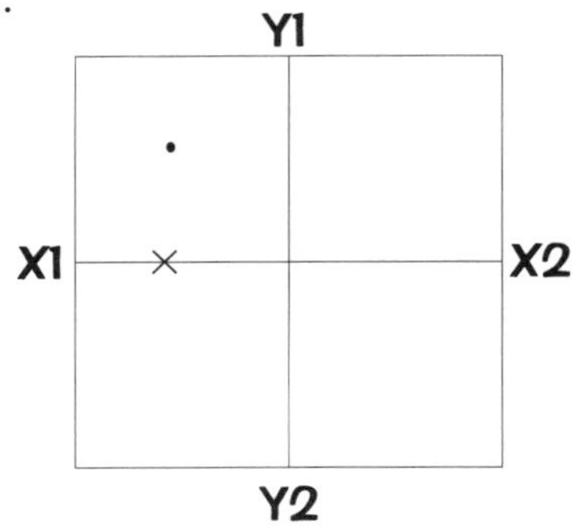

a) Draw in the position of the electron beam if the connections to X1 and X2 are swapped round so that a positive potential is connected to X2 and Y1.

b) The following points describe how the voltages across the charged metal plates change over time. Sketch the path of the electron beam that would result from this sequence of changes.

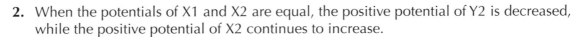

1. The positive potential of X2 is increased while the positive potential of Y2 is also increased.
2. When the potentials of X1 and X2 are equal, the positive potential of Y2 is decreased, while the positive potential of X2 continues to increase.
3. The voltage changes stop when the potentials of Y1 and Y2 are equal. At this point X2 is more positive than X1.

Q5 The diagram below shows a machine for taking **dental X-rays**.

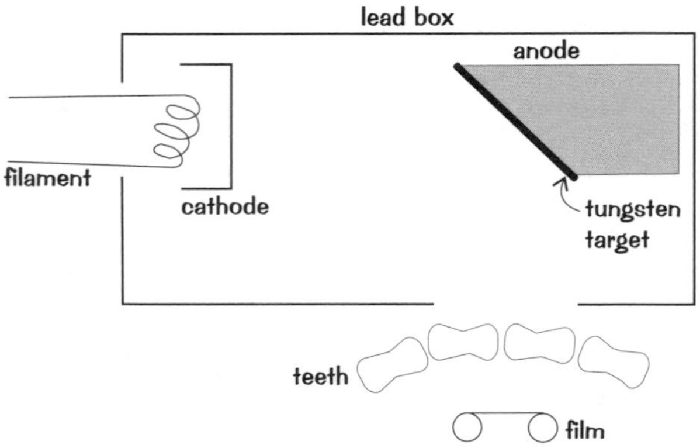

a) Sketch in and label the **path of the electron beam** on the diagram. Show the direction of the beam.

b) Sketch in and label the **path of the X-rays** on the diagram. Show the direction of the beam.

c) At the **anode** the electrons from the beam strike atoms of tungsten, causing them to emit **X-rays**. Where does the energy for the X-rays come from?

....

....

Q6 Scientists at CERN use an enormous **particle accelerator** to smash particles into each other at tremendous speeds.

a) When the factors below are **increased** will the **deflection** of a beam of charged particles increase, decrease or remain unchanged? Connect each factor with its effect on the deflection.

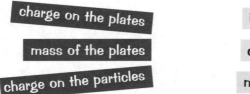

charge on the plates	increase	mass of the particles
mass of the plates	decrease	
charge on the particles	no change	speed of the particles

b) Give two reasons why scientists from all over Europe collaborate on the research at CERN.

....

....

Medical Uses of Light

Q1 The diagram below shows a **pulse oximeter** on a hospital patient's **finger**.

a) Add arrows to the diagram to show the direction of the red light and infrared beams.

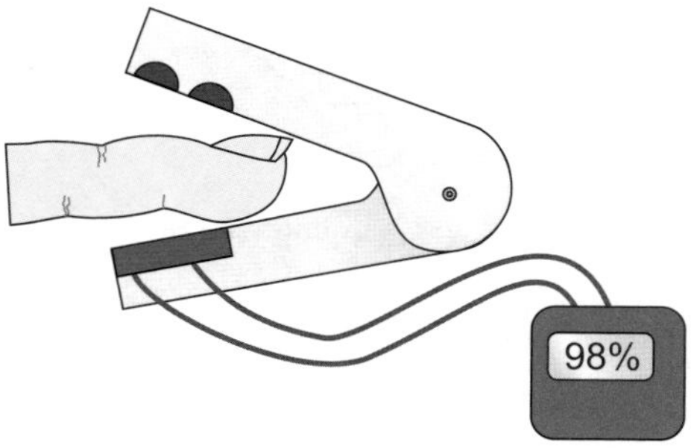

b) Choose from the words given below to complete the passage about how a pulse oximeter works.

reflected	reduced	absorbed	calibrated
monkey	tissue	increased	

Red and infrared light pass through the .... and are detected by a photo detector. Some of the light is .... by the red blood, so the amount of light detected by the detector is .... The amount of light absorbed depends on the amount of oxyhaemoglobin in the blood so the display can be .... to show the blood's oxyhaemoglobin content.

c) State one other suitable part of the **body** where a pulse oximeter could be placed. Explain your answer.

....

....

Q2 Doctors use **endoscopes** to look inside patients' bodies. Endoscopes work using **optical fibres**.

a) What **material** could the optical fibres in an endoscope be made from?

....

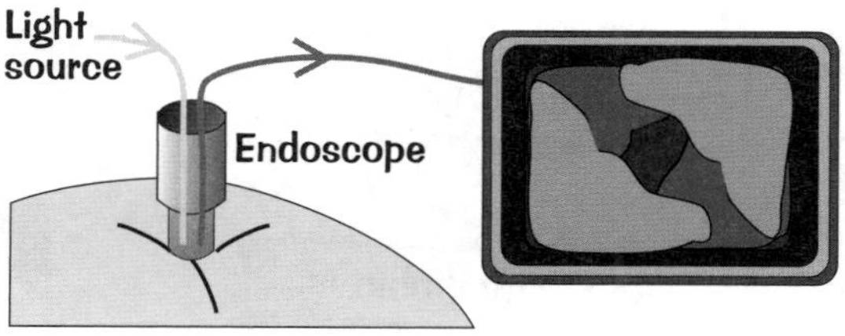

b) Explain why doctors try not to **bend** an endoscope sharply.

....

....

Medical Uses of Light

Q3 The diagram shows the use of an **endoscope** in **keyhole surgery**.

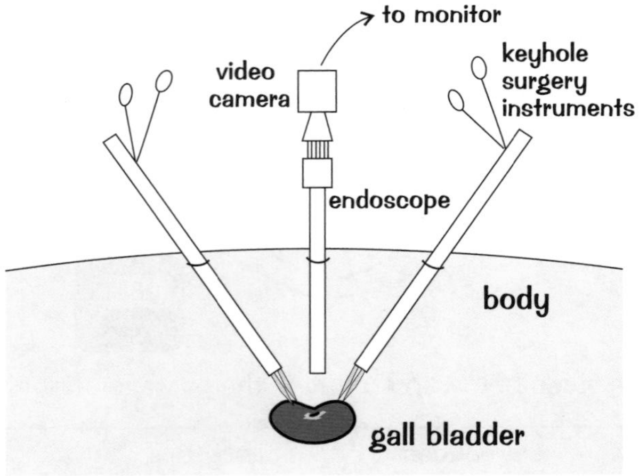

a) Explain what is meant by the term **keyhole surgery**.

b) Outline how an endoscope works.

c) Give two **advantages** of keyhole surgery over conventional surgery.

Q4 **Reflection** pulse oximetry is used to measure the amount of oxygen in the blood.

a) How does reflection pulse oximetry differ from the type of pulse oximetry described in question 1?

b) Connect the boxes below to complete the sentences about haemoglobin.

Oxyhaemoglobin is...	...purply coloured...	...and doesn't contain much oxygen.
Reduced haemoglobin is...	...bright red...	...and rich in oxygen.

Top Tips: When you're learning about endoscopes, impress your friends by casually dropping the word 'esophagogastroduodenoscopy' into conversation. It means using an endoscope to have a look all the way down someone's throat right to their guts – mmm, nice.

Energy and Metabolic Rate

Q1 The table shows some activities and the **metabolic rates** associated with them.

Activity	kJ/min
Sleeping	4.5
Watching TV	
Cycling (15 mph)	21
Jogging (5 mph)	40
Slow walking	14

a) What does metabolic rate mean?

....

....

b) Complete the table by inserting a suitable metabolic rate for **watching TV**.

c) i) Suggest three processes within a person's body that require energy while they're watching TV.

....

ii) Where does the energy for these processes come from?

....

Q2 Ed says that his metabolic rate must be lowest just after lunch because this is when he has the most trouble paying attention in lessons, so his body must be transferring energy to his brain very slowly.

a) Explain how Ed's reasoning is incorrect.

....

b) A person's lowest metabolic rate is called the **basal metabolic rate** or BMR.

i) What does BMR measure in terms of the processes going on in a person's body?

....

ii) Outline how to measure Ed's BMR and show him that his metabolic rate is higher after lunch.

....

....

....

Q3 It takes Denny three minutes to jog up a hill. His metabolic rate as he jogs is **50 kJ/min**.

a) How much energy does Denny need for this jog?

....

b) Calculate the potential energy Denny gains by reaching the top of the hill.

....

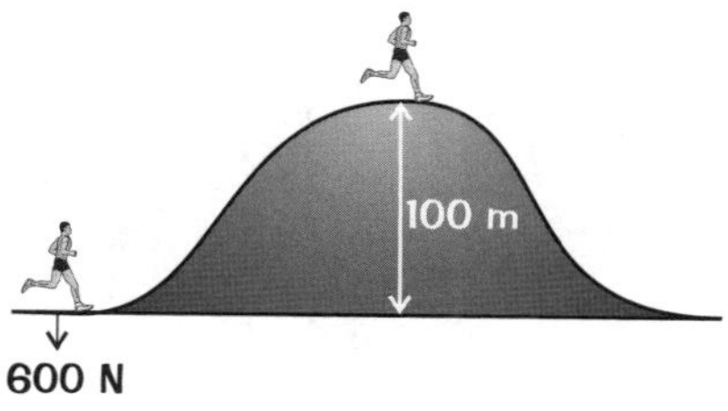

c) Explain why the energy needed by Denny to jog up the hill is greater than the potential energy he gains.

....

....

Energy and Metabolic Rate

Q4 The graph below shows how the **basal metabolic rates** of Joanna and her mum vary over time.

a) Joanna is 6 years old and her mum is 34. Use your knowledge of how BMR varies with **age** to label the graph. Use **J** for Joanna and **M** for her mum.

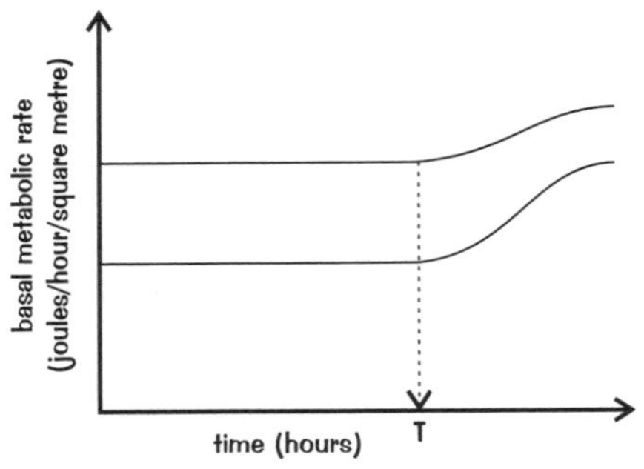

b) The graph shows that both Joanna and her mum's BMRs began to rise at time T.

i) Suggest what may have happened at **time T** to cause this.

....

ii) What physical factor may have caused Joanna and her mum's BMRs to increase at different rates, as shown by the graph?

....

Q5 Chloe's doctor advises her to try to lose some weight. Her friend suggests she should reduce her food consumption from 3000 to 300 kcal per day.

a) **i)** Explain the effect such a dramatic reduction in energy intake would have on Chloe's BMR.

....

ii) Why would this not help Chloe lose as much weight as she might expect?

....

b) Chloe's doctor tells her that reducing her energy intake this much is a really bad way to lose weight, and could be harmful. He says she should start exercising as well as changing her eating habits. Give **two** reasons why exercise can help people to lose weight.

....

....

Q6 Dr Mayer worked with patients who travelled between Europe and Indonesia in the 20th century. He realised that his patients had a lower metabolic rate when they were in Indonesia than they had in Europe.

Explain how the difference between the European and tropical Indonesian climates caused this effect.

....

....

Electricity and the Body

Q1 Sharma is in hospital to have an **electromyogram** (**EMG**) of the muscles in her legs. The muscles have become weaker recently, and her doctor thinks she may have **muscular dystrophy**.

a) What does an EMG machine measure?

....

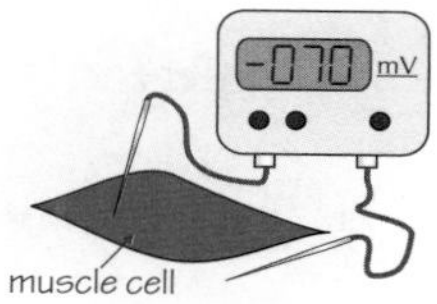

b) Define the following terms:

i) resting potential ....

....

ii) action potential ....

....

c) What value would you expect to record from a **contracted** muscle cell in a healthy person? ....

Q2 Electrocardiographs (ECGs) are used to measure the activity of the **heart**.

a) Describe, briefly, the **structure** of the heart.

....

b) Explain how a series of electrical signals help to produce a heart beat.

....

....

c) Describe the sensors used to detect the action potentials of a patient's heart.

....

Q3 The diagram below shows a typical **ECG**.

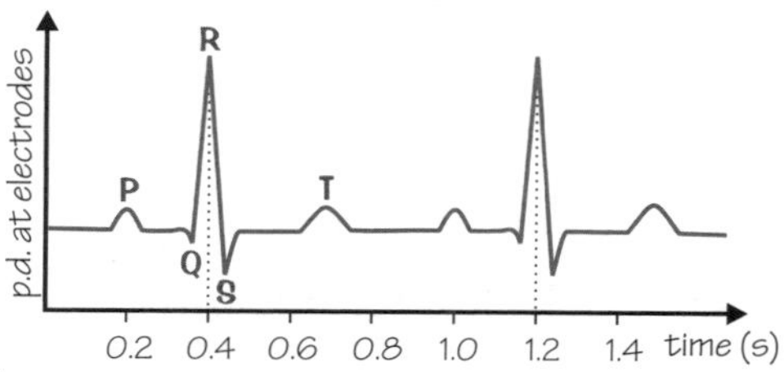

a) Show the size of the **resting potential** with an arrow on the y-axis.

b) What is the **period** of the heartbeat? ....

c) Calculate the frequency of the heartbeat in **beats per minute.**

....

d) What **muscle action** in the heart is being recorded at points:

i) P ....

ii) QRS ....

iii) T ....

Intensity of Radiation

Q1 The word '**radiation**' is often used to refer to nuclear sources, but it also covers many other types.

a) Sort the following forms of radiation according to their properties.

infrared

neutron

alpha

X-rays

visible light

gamma

beta

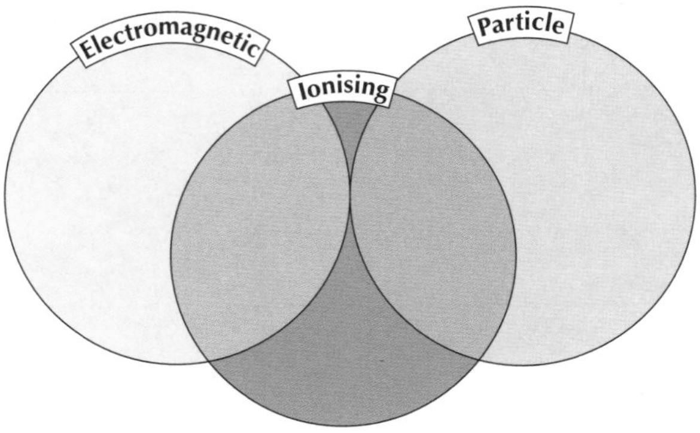

b) Define radiation.

....

Q2 Jonny is watching Kill Phil using a projector and a screen. The bulb in his projector gives an intensity of **8 W/m²** on the projector screen in its current position.

a) Write down the intensity of radiation on the screen if the distance between the bulb and screen is:

i) doubled. ....

ii) halved. ....

iii) quadrupled. ....

b) Write down the intensity of radiation on the screen if the power of the bulb is doubled.

....

Q3 Sam and Amy have made a spherical lantern for the Halloween parade. The lantern has a **diameter** of **40 cm** and contains a candle with a power of **0.8 W** at its centre.

a) Calculate the surface area of the lantern in square metres.

....

....

Remember the surface area of a sphere = $4/3\,\pi\,r^2$

b) Calculate the **intensity** of the light radiation on the inside surface of the lantern.

....

c) How will the intensity of the light from the candle reaching the outside surface of the lantern compare to that reaching the inside surface? Explain your answer.

....

Top Tips: If this intensity of radiation malarkey is just not making sense, try getting a torch out and seeing it in action. Hold your hand up close to the torch, what do you see — a bright spot of light. Shine it on a wall at school, guess what — a large patch of dim light.

Nuclear Bombardment

Q1 Uranium-235 atoms are split in nuclear reactors to release energy. Some products of the fission can also be used for medical applications.

a) Uranium-235 must be converted to uranium-236 using a thermal neutron.

i) What is a thermal neutron?

....

ii) Describe how uranium-235 is converted into uranium-236.

....

b) U-236 splits into two smaller atoms, which are often unstable. What makes these atoms unstable?

....

c) Suggest one medical application for the products of the fission of uranium-235.

....

Q2 Bombarding stable elements with **protons** can produce **radioactive isotopes**. Complete the following passage using the words provided.

nucleus	accelerator	cyclotron	electron	proton	element	mass

A proton is absorbed by the .... This increases its .... number so a new .... is produced. The proton needs a lot of energy before it can be absorbed by the nucleus, so this process takes place in a particle .... called a ....

Q3 The radioisotopes produced by proton bombardment are **unstable**.

a) Complete the following equations to show how two radioisotopes are formed.

$${}^{18}_{8}O + {}^{1}_{1}p \longrightarrow {}^{\square}_{\square}F + {}^{1}_{0}n \qquad {}^{14}_{7}N + {}^{1}_{1}p \longrightarrow {}^{\square}_{\square}C + {}^{4}_{2}He$$

b) i) What sort of radiation do the radioisotopes formed in this way usually emit?

....

ii) Suggest a medical use for these radioisotopes.

....

iii) Explain why some hospitals have their own facilities for producing these radioisotopes.

....

Momentum Conservation

Q1 The diagram shows a fast moving **neutron colliding** with a stationary sodium **nucleus** and bouncing off again.

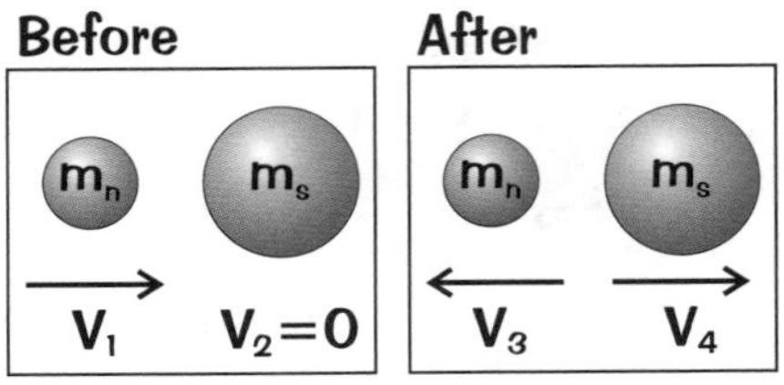

a) Using the notation in the diagram, write an expression for:

i) the total momentum before the collision.

....

ii) the total momentum after the collision.

....

b) Using your answers to part a), explain what is meant by the term **conservation of momentum**.

....

Q2 The diagram below shows the **collision** of a neutron and an atom of uranium-235.

Use the relative masses in your calculations.

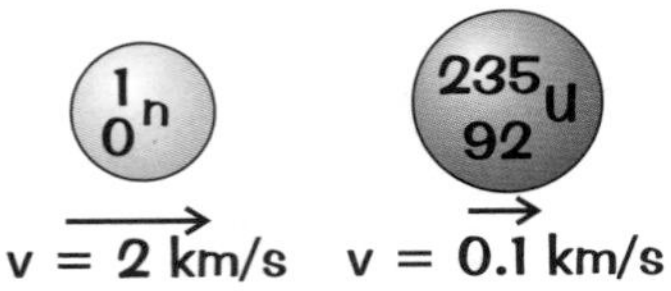

a) Calculate the relative momentum of the:

i) neutron. ....

ii) uranium-235 nucleus. ....

b) The uranium-235 nucleus absorbs the neutron to form uranium-236.
What is the relative momentum of the uranium-236 isotope?

....

Q3 The diagram shows the **alpha decay** of **uranium-238**.

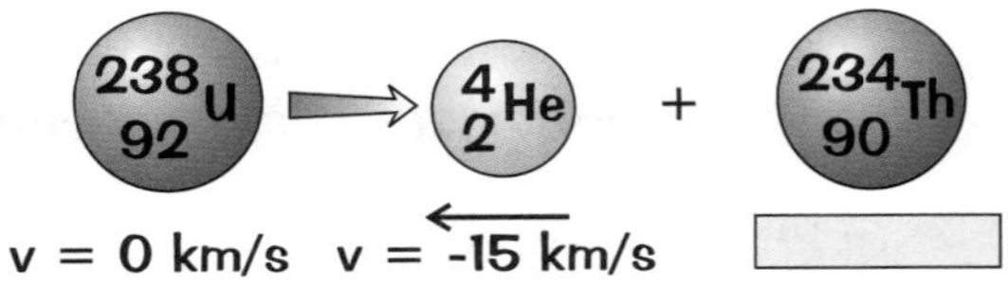

a) **i)** Add an arrow to the diagram to show which way the **thorium** nucleus will move.

ii) Explain why it must move this way.

....

b) Calculate the **velocity** of the thorium nucleus immediately after the decay.

....

Q4 The diagram represents the **collision** of an **electron** and a **positron**.

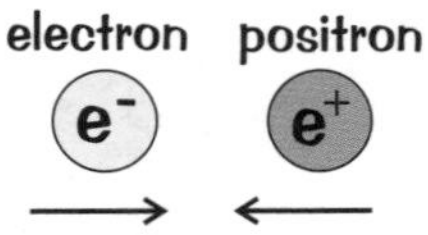

a) Choose the correct words from each pair to complete the sentences below.

> The collision of an electron and a positron produces a pair of **gamma rays / radioactive particles**. The **gamma rays / radioactive particles** produced have the same **energy / velocity** as each other, and opposite **energies / velocities**.

b) Explain how this collision is an example of mass/energy conservation.

....

....

Medical Uses of Radiation

Q1 **Positron emission tomography** (PET) is a scanning technique used in hospitals.

a) Give one advantage and one disadvantage of PET compared to X-rays.

i) advantage: ....

ii) disadvantage: ....

b) Give two conditions that can be researched using PET.

....

Q2 Put the following stages in the right order to explain how PET is carried out.

- [ ] **The radiotracer moves through the body to the organs.**
- [ ] **Detectors around the body record the position of the emitted gamma rays.**
- [ ] **The patient is injected with the radiotracer.**
- [ ] **The positrons collide with electrons and are annihilated, releasing gamma rays.**
- [ ] **The radioisotope emits positrons.**
- [1] **A positron-emitting radioactive isotope is added to a substance used by the body to make a radiotracer.**
- [ ] **A computer builds up a map of radioactivity in the body.**

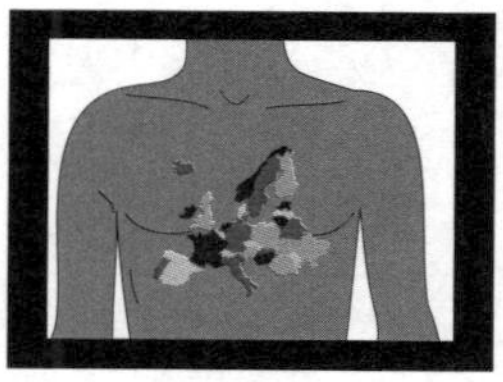

Q3 The **map of radioactivity** in the body produced by a PET scan can be used to detect active cancer tumours.

a) **i)** What does the map of radioactivity match up with?

....

ii) Why is this?

....

b) Explain why a PET scan is a good way to detect cancer.

....

c) Why is PET not used frequently on the same patient?

....

Q4 **Radiation exposure** can be damaging, but is also used as a medical treatment.

a) Explain how radiotherapy can be used as a form of **palliative care**.

....

....

b) Describe **two** ways in which radiation can damage cells.

....

Medical Research

Q1 Draw lines to match each medical **technique** on the left to the medical **condition** or process each might be used in.

Endoscope | Keyhole surgery
ECG | Monitoring heart conditions
PET | Mutating bacteria
Antibiotic development | Locating cancer cells

Q2 Imagine a new drug has been developed to treat breast cancer. It has been tested on people with end-stage breast cancer, and shown to be an effective treatment with tolerable side effects.

a) The drug has not been tested on people with early-stage breast cancer.

i) Why might someone with early-stage breast cancer want to take this drug?

....

ii) Suggest why doctors would be unwilling to give this drug to patients with early-stage breast cancer.

....

b) An alternative treatment for breast cancer is radiotherapy. However, there are environmental issues, as well as unpleasant side effects, associated with radiotherapy. Outline one such issue.

....

Q3 The cost in poorer countries of drugs for treating AIDS has recently fallen significantly. This is largely due to sales of **copies** of branded drugs, called **generic drugs**. These are cheaper because the company producing them did not have to pay the cost of the drug's development.

a) Explain how the sale of **generic drugs** might lead to the development of fewer new drugs.

....

....

b) Part a) gives an argument against making generic drugs. Outline one other argument **against** and one argument **for** the distribution of generic drugs in poorer countries.

i) Against: ....

....

ii) For: ....

....

c) The drugs currently available treat the symptoms of AIDS, but do not cure the disease. Suggest one ethical issue that might arise if a cure for AIDS was being developed.

....

Answers

Section One — Heat and Energy

Section One — Heat and Energy

Page 1 — Moving and Storing Heat

Q1 Heat is a measure of **energy**.
Temperature is a measure of **hotness**.
Heat travels from a **hot** place to a **cold** place.
Water is a good material for storing heat because it has a **high** specific heat capacity.
When a substance is heated its particles vibrate **more** quickly.

Q2 a) Any one of Celsius, Fahrenheit, Kelvin

b) Heat is measured on an absolute scale. Zero heat means zero movement of particles, and you can't have less than zero movement.

Q3 a) Specific heat capacity is the amount of energy needed to raise the temperature of 1 kg of a substance by 1 °C.

b) Substance A (substances with a high specific heat capacity release more heat as they cool down).

Q4 Energy = Mass × SHC × temperature change.
The temperature change for both is 50 °C.
Energy from mercury = 27.2 × 139 × 50 = 189 040 J
Energy from water = 2 × 4200 × 50 = 420 000 J
Difference = 420 000 – 189 040 = **230 960 J**.

Q5 Rearrange the energy equation:
Mass = Energy ÷ (SHC × temperature change).
Mass = 3040 ÷ (380 × 40) = 3040 ÷ 15 200
= **0.2 kg** of copper (or **200 g**).

Pages 2-3 — Melting and Boiling

Q1 Boiling — D
Gas — E
Liquid — C
Melting — B
Solid — A

Q2 C

Q3 a) 60 °C

b) Bonds are forming between particles, which releases energy. This stops the wax from cooling.

c) 15 minutes

Q4 To evaporate this mass of water would need 1.5 × 2 260 000 J of energy = 3 390 000 J. The kettle supplies 2 500 J every second, so would need to be on for 3 390 000 ÷ 2500 s = **1356 s** (22.6 minutes).

Q5 a) i) Ice needs 334 kJ of energy to melt 1 kg, so 500 kJ of energy would melt 500 ÷ 334 kg = **1.5 kg** (to 2 s.f.) of ice.

ii) 500 ÷ 118 kg = **4.2 kg** (to 2 s.f.) of zinc.

b) 30 g of ice completely melts (the mass and exact temp. of the lemonade don't matter). Energy = mass × specific latent heat = 0.03 × 334 000 = **10 020 J**.

Page 4 — Conduction and Convection

Q1 a) True
b) False
c) True
d) False

Q2 The piece of wood feels quite warm because wood is a poor conductor, so it does not conduct much heat energy away from George's hand. The metal spoon feels colder because metal is a good conductor, so it conducts heat energy away from his hand very quickly.

Q3 The string vest (or the pockets of trapped air) makes his clothing less conductive / it traps pockets of air, which is a poor conductor (a good insulator).

Q4 The very bottom of a hot water tank stays cold... because water doesn't conduct much heat.
Warm air rises... because it is not so dense.
A small heater can send heat all over a room... because heat flows from warm places to cooler ones.

Q5 The experiment shows that convection works very well in water — the ice melts at the top because convection currents carry warm water upwards. It also shows that water is a poor conductor of heat — convection currents do not warm the water below the flame, and the water below the heater stays cold because conduction only occurs very slowly.

Pages 5-6 — Heat Radiation

Q1 a) i) True
ii) False
iii) False

b) ii) Hot objects do absorb radiation.
iii) Cold objects do emit radiation (but much less than hot objects).

Q2 Flask B will cool fastest because it has the largest temperature difference between the water and the air in the box.

Q3 a) Peter is **wrong** because **radiation** is the only way heat can get across the vacuum of space.

b) Lucy is **right** because heat travels from hotter regions to cooler regions.

Q4 a) False
b) True
c) True
d) False
e) False

Q5 a) i), ii) and iii)

Surface	Reading	Colour and Texture
A	10	**matt black**
B	4	dull silver
C	4	**shiny white**
D	2	**shiny silver**

b) i) D — because it emits least radiation and will make the kettle most efficient at heating the water inside.
ii) D — because it emits (and will absorb) least radiation and so will be best at keeping the food inside cool.
iii) A — because it emits most radiation and so will allow the engine to cool fastest.

Page 7 — Saving Energy

Q1 Through the roof — loft insulation.
Through the walls — cavity wall insulation.
Through the doors — double glazing of any glass panels or draught-proofing strips around the frames and letter box.

Q2 a) Payback time = 1200 ÷ 20 = 60 years.

b) No, because although the shutters are cheaper they are less cost-effective / they have a longer payback time.

c) Fit draught-proofing strips around the windows.
Hang thick curtains.

Q3 a) It reduces heat transfer by convection, because pockets of air are trapped in the foam and can't move between the two walls. It also reduces radiation across the gap.

b) Layers of fibreglass wool reduce heat transfer by conduction from the ceiling to the roof space. Heat transfer by radiation is also reduced, because the loft floor is not so warm.

Page 8 — Energy Transfer

Q1 a) **chemical energy** → heat energy
b) electrical energy → **sound energy**
c) **electrical energy** → **light energy**

Q2 conservation, resources, run out, principle, stay the same.

Q3 a) i) chemical energy
ii) heat/thermal energy (and kinetic energy)

Section One — Heat and Energy

b) Any two from:
Chemical energy → heat energy (as the coal burns).
Heat energy → kinetic energy (as the steam drives the engine).
Chemical energy → light energy (in the lamp).
Other answers are possible.

Q4 a) gravitational potential energy

b) Chemical energy from the porridge is converted to kinetic energy in Bruce's muscles and the moving bar. This kinetic energy is then converted to gravitational potential energy.

c) It is converted into kinetic energy as the bar falls downwards.

Pages 9-10 — Energy Transformation Diagrams

Q1 a) 10 J

b) 150 J

Q2 See diagram below — where the scale is 1 small square = 2 J. Different scales are possible.

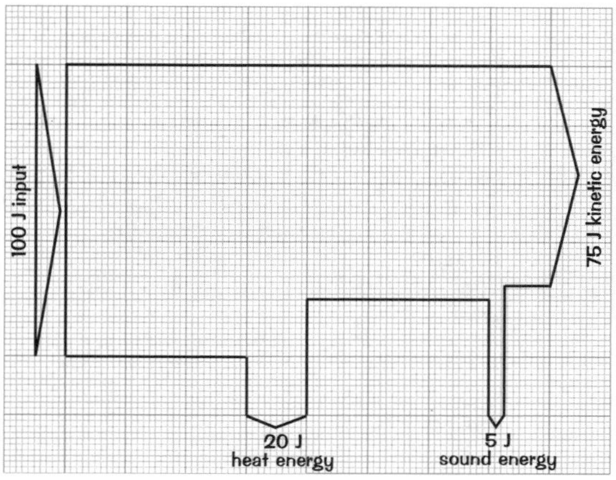

Q3 1. The input energy is not shown clearly. The 100 J kinetic energy should be shown as input energy.
2. The quantities of energy do not add up. The electrical energy plus the waste heat energy should equal the input energy. Either the input should be 125 J, or the heat wasted should be 25 J.

Q4 a) 100 J heat + 40 J GPE = **140 J**

b) 60 J

c) Efficiency = 60 ÷ 200 = **0.3**.

Page 11 — Efficiency

Q1 convert, useful, heat, fraction, input, output

Q2 a) 100 J

b) 5 J

c) 95 J

d) 5%

Q3

Total Energy Input (J)	Useful Energy Output (J)	Efficiency
2000	1500	**0.75**
4000	2000	0.50
4000	**1000**	0.25
600	200	**0.33**
2500	500	0.20
200	**180**	0.90

Q4 The winch, like all other devices, is not 100% efficient — some of the input energy will be 'wasted'. Much of this waste is likely to be heat energy, generated by friction in the motor and between the moving parts of the winch.

Page 12 — Energy Sources

Q1 a) E.g. Renewable resources won't ever run out, whereas non-renewable resources will eventually run out / cannot be replenished when they are used up.

b) The following (renewables) should be circled:
tidal, waves, solar, biomass, hydroelectric, wind, geothermal
The following (non-renewables) should be underlined:
coal, natural gas, nuclear, oil

Q2 a) Acid rain — sulfur dioxide formed by burning oil and coal
Climate change — releasing CO_2 by burning fossil fuels
Dangerous radioactive waste — using nuclear power
Spoiling of natural landscapes — coal mining OR sulfur dioxide formed by burning oil and coal

b) E.g. Fossil fuels and nuclear energy power are more reliable than many renewable energy sources. / Fossil fuels are relatively cheap and plentiful.

Q3 a) i) E.g. The energy in biomass (plants, animals or animal waste) is chemical energy. Plants turn the Sun's energy into chemical energy (by photosynthesis). The plants may then be consumed by animals.

ii) E.g. The energy in waves is kinetic energy. Waves are caused by the wind, which is generated by the Sun — air is warmed by the Sun and rises, and then colder air (wind) rushes in to take its place.

b) Nuclear — energy locked up in the nuclei of atoms.
Geothermal — heat from the nuclear decay of radioactive elements inside the Earth.
Tidal — the gravitational pull of the Moon (and the Sun).

Page 13 — Nuclear and Geothermal Energy

Q1 a) A nuclear reactor uses **uranium** (or **plutonium**) to make heat.

b) Nuclear power stations are **more expensive** to build than coal fired power stations and they **take longer** to start up.

Q2 E.g. Nuclear power stations don't produce greenhouse gases / contribute to global warming. Nuclear fuels (uranium) are likely to be readily available for longer than fossil fuels.

Q3 Any two from: Nuclear power stations are expensive to build. There is a risk of catastrophic accidents. Nuclear power stations may be a target for terrorists.
It produces radioactive waste which is dangerous and hard to get rid of (or reprocess). Processing spent nuclear fuel causes pollution. Old/worn out nuclear power stations have to be decommissioned and this is expensive.

Q4 a) 1) It is sealed into glass blocks.
2) The blocks are sealed into metal canisters.

b) The site mustn't be prone to earthquakes because earthquakes could break canisters of radioactive material and let the material leak out. Radioactive material could get into ground water.

Q5 a) False

b) True

c) False

d) False

Page 14 — Wind and Solar Energy

Q1 a) Any two from: They make a lot of noise. They spoil the view/landscape. They only work if it's windy. The electricity they generate is expensive. A lot of turbines are needed to replace one power station.

b) Any two from: Once running, they don't create any pollution. There's no permanent damage to the landscape. They use a renewable, free source of energy. Running costs are low. They don't emit greenhouse gases.

Section Two — Electricity and Waves

Q2 silicon, semiconductor, atoms, electrons, electrons, DC

Q3 Advantages — they use a renewable and free source of energy (there are no fuel costs), they are a good way to provide energy in remote places, there is no pollution when they are in use. Disadvantages — the initial costs are high, most solar cells are not very efficient, they don't work well when it's cloudy.

Q4 a) i) A matt black surface absorbs solar radiation well.

ii) The glass box lets the light and heat in (and keeps cold air out).

b) This is done to keep the panel pointing directly at the Sun, so that it absorbs more light and heat and is more effective at heating the water.

Pages 15-16 — Biomass, Wave and Tidal Energy

Q1 a) Tidal

b) Wave

c) Tidal

d) Wave

e) Tidal

Q2 a) When the tide comes in the water passes through the turbines and then builds up behind the barrage. When the tide goes out the water is allowed out through the turbines in the barrage at a controlled speed. As the water passes through the turbines, electricity is generated. (The water also turns the turbines on the way in.)

b) E.g. any two from: Barrages can look unattractive. Barrages can prevent access for boats. Barrages can damage habitats. Initial costs are fairly high.

Q3 a)
1. A wave moves water upwards, forcing air out towards a turbine.
2. The moving air makes the turbine spin.
3. The spinning turbine drives a generator.
4. The spinning generator makes electricity.
5. The water goes down again.
6. Air is sucked downwards, spinning the turbine the other way and generating more power.

b) Any two from: High initial costs. Spoiling the view. Can be unreliable because it depends on winds. It is currently only suitable for small-scale use. Can be a hazard to boats.

Q4 a) E.g. The droppings are burnt to heat water, producing steam which turns turbines that spin a generator. OR The droppings are fermented to produce methane which can be burnt to heat water, etc.

b) Chicken droppings will not run out — more chickens can always be bred and more corn, etc. can be grown to feed them.

c) E.g. any two from: straw, other farm waste, kitchen waste, specially grown forests.

d) The amount of carbon dioxide released on burning the biomass is the same amount that was taken in by the plant as it grew, so overall the amount of CO_2 in the atmosphere doesn't increase.

Q5 a) Gas (usually methane or ethanol) which is produced by fermenting biomass.

b) cattle dung

c) Burn the gas in a generator to produce electricity.

Q6 E.g. Fiza, because burning landfill rubbish releases toxic gases like sulfur dioxide and nitrogen oxide.
OR Julie, because burning the biomass in landfill rubbish is carbon neutral, whereas burning coal contributes to global warming as well as releasing other pollutants such as sulfur dioxide.

Page 17 — Hydroelectric and Pumped Storage

Q1
1. At night big power stations make more electricity than is needed.
2. Spare electricity is used to pump water from reservoirs at a low level to others at a high level.
3. Water at a high level stores energy until it is needed.
4. At peak times water is allowed to flow downhill, powering turbines and generating electricity.

Q2 Big coal-fired power stations deliver energy... all the time.
Pumped storage power stations deliver energy... that they have previously stored / when it is needed.
Hydroelectric power stations deliver electricity... when it is needed.

Q3 a) **Agree** — e.g. no pollution is produced when electricity is being generated. OR
Disagree — e.g. building the dams and manufacturing the turbines, generators, etc. does cause pollution.

b) **Agree** — e.g. there are no fuel costs. OR
Disagree — e.g. building dams and purchasing turbines, etc. is expensive.

c) **Agree** — e.g. dams are unsightly; they disturb the natural environment and disrupt wildlife, etc. OR
Disagree — e.g. an impressive engineering structure has a positive visual impact; not all hydroelectric projects involve building dams.

d) **Agree** — e.g. it is rare for reservoirs to be empty even in dry weather, and water can be released to power the generators when it's needed most. OR
Disagree — e.g. power supplies are less reliable during droughts, and this may be a more serious problem in the future.

e) Any one from: it is a renewable source of energy, it does not contribute to global warming (once running), the output can be varied more quickly than that of most other power stations.

Section Two — Electricity and Waves

Page 18 — Electric Current

Q1 electrons, voltage, voltage (or resistance), resistance (or voltage)

Q2
a) the flow of water
b) a battery / cell (which provides a voltage)
c) constrictions in the circuit
d) The flow of water would increase.
Increasing the voltage.

Q3 a) E.g.

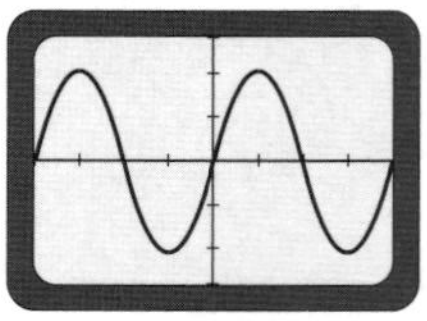

b) E.g.

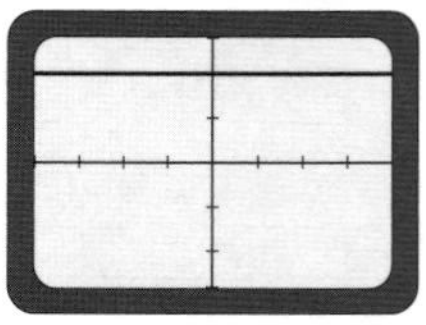

Section Two — Electricity and Waves

Page 19 — Current, Voltage and Resistance

Q1 a) increases
b) decreases

Q2 a)

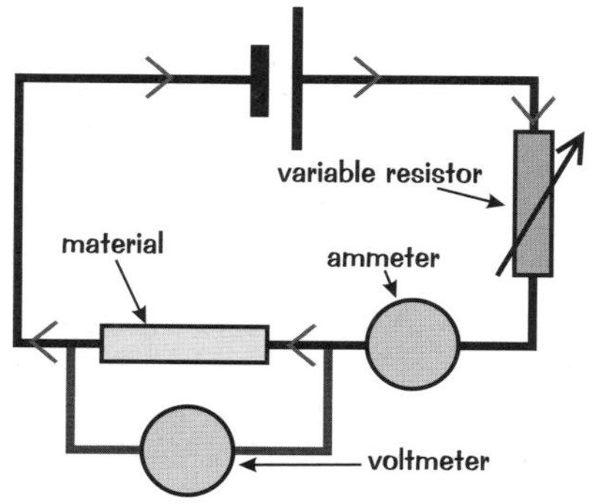

b) R = V ÷ I = 6 ÷ 2.4 = 2.5 Ω
c) He would need to change the resistance of the variable resistor several times and each time take readings from the ammeter and voltmeter. Each of these pairs of readings would allow him to calculate the resistance of the material. Repeating the experiment like this will increase the reliability of his result.

Q3

Voltage (V)	Current (A)	Resistance (Ω)
6	2	3
8	4	2
9	3	3
4	8	0.5
2	0.5	4
1	0.5	2

Pages 20-21 — The Dynamo Effect

Q1 a) Move the (vertical) wire in and out of the magnetic field at an angle to the direction of the field (i.e. not parallel to the magnetic field).
b) The ammeter needle would move first in one direction, then back to zero and then in the opposite direction and back to zero again. It would continue like this as long as the wire was moving in and out of the magnetic field.
c) i) The ammeter would still move from one side to the other, but would start from the opposite side.
ii) The effect would be the same as in i) above.
Q2 a) It reverses direction.
b) a current / potential difference (voltage)
c) AC
Q3 a) By pulling the magnet out again OR by turning the magnet round and pushing it into the coil OR by pushing the magnet into the coil from the left-hand side OR by turning the magnet around and pulling it out of the left-hand side of the coil.
b) By pushing the magnet in and immediately pulling it out again.
c) By rapidly pushing the magnet in and out of the coil a number of times.
d) Kinetic energy from the moving magnet is transferred via its magnetic field into electrical energy in the wire, which is then carried to the oscilloscope.
Q4 Generator **A** should be ticked.

Page 22 — Power Stations and the National Grid

Q1 power stations, National, Grid, generated, consumers, farms
Q2
1. A fossil fuel such as coal is burned to release heat.
2. Water is heated in the boiler and turned to steam.
3. Hot steam rushes through a turbine and makes it spin.
4. The spinning turbine makes the generator spin too.
5. Electricity is produced by the spinning generator.

Q3 a) The National Grid transmits energy at high voltage and **low current**.
b) A step-up transformer is used to **raise the voltage** of the supply before electricity is transmitted.
c) Using a **low current** makes sure there is not much energy wasted.
Q4 a) AC
b) Voltage is stepped up or down with transformers — these only work with AC.

Page 23 — Electrical Power

Q1

Appliance	Power (W)	Current (A)
Kettle	2600	11.3
Radio	13	0.057
Laptop computer	736	3.2
Lamp	39.1	0.17

Q2 a) Units of energy = power × time = 2 kW × 3 h = **6 kWh**.
b) Cost = 6 kWh × 7p/kWh = **42p**.
c) Lamp: Energy used = 0.06 kW × 9 h = 0.54 kWh.
Shower: Energy used = 8 kW × 0.25 h = 2 kWh.
So **Boris is right** — the shower uses more energy.
Q3 a) 34783 – 34259 = **524 Units**.
b) Total cost = 524 × 9.7 = **5083p** (= **£50.83**).

Pages 24-25 — Waves

Q1 a) A and C
b) A and B
c) A and C
Q2 a) False
b) False
c) False
d) False
Q3 Transverse:
vibrations are at 90° to the direction of travel of the wave,
produced by a slinky spring whose end is wiggled at 90° to the spring itself,
ripples on water,
electromagnetic radiation.
Longitudinal:
vibrations are along the same direction as the wave is travelling,
sound waves,
produced by a slinky spring whose end is pushed and pulled towards and away from the rest of the spring.
Q4 Similarities: e.g.
They are both electromagnetic radiation.
They have a similar wavelength/wavelength in the order of 10^{-7} metres (in fact, it's about 4×10^{-7} m for violet and 7×10^{-7} m for red).
Differences: e.g.
Their wavelengths are different (even though they're similar).
We see them as different colours.

Section Two — Electricity and Waves

Q5

a)

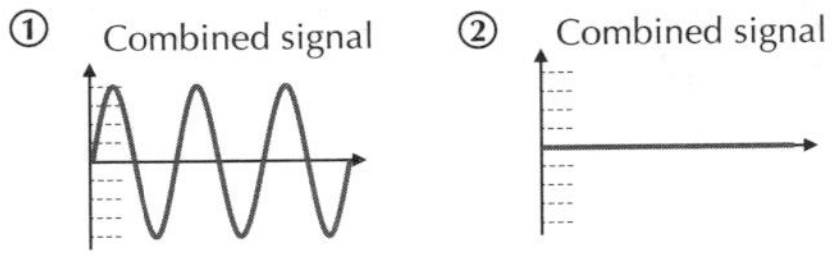

b) 'wavelength' (or 'frequency')
'180° (or completely) out of'

c) The two radio signals may interfere with each other because they are on similar frequencies.

Q6 a) Diffraction
b) Reflection
c) Refraction

Page 26 — Refraction

Q1 a) diagram B
b) Because the wave meets the boundary at right angles.
c) It gets shorter.
d) It stays the same.
e) The wave slows down (because the wavelength gets smaller but the frequency stays the same).
f) The wave would speed up again (to the same velocity it had before entering the denser medium).

Q2 a) In the left-hand diagram, the angle of incidence is 46° (greater than the critical angle of 42°), so the ray is totally internally reflected. In the second diagram, the angle of incidence is 30°, so the ray is partially reflected, but most of the light passes out of the glass.

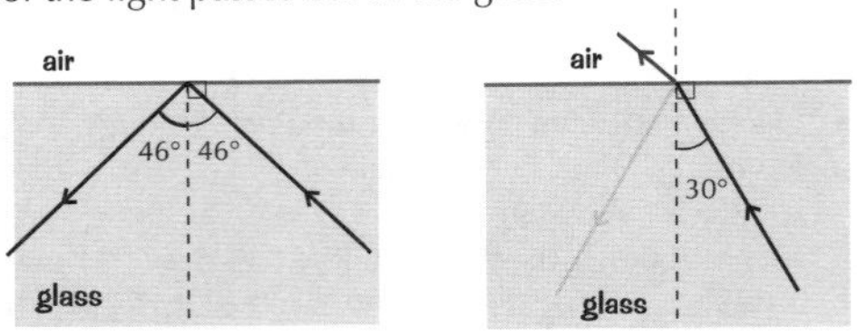

b) If the tube is bent too much, the angle of incidence may be below the critical angle, letting light escape.

Page 27 — Dangers of EM Radiation

Q1 Helpful — any two from: communications, cooking, medical diagnosis, killing cancer cells in radiotherapy, photosynthesis, detecting cracks. Or other sensible answers.
Harmful — any two from: cause cell mutations, kill cells and cause radiation sickness, cause cancer, burn skin, damage eyes. Or other sensible answers.

Q2 a) The energy is directly proportional to the frequency of the wave (or vice versa).
b) A — radio waves
B — green light
C — gamma radiation

Q3 a) Although they do produce UV waves, these are mostly absorbed by special coatings inside the tubes so very little UV is emitted from the lights.
b) Dark skin absorbs more of the harmful radiation and prevents it from penetrating deeper and damaging more vulnerable tissues.
c) Radiographers are exposed to X-rays every day that they work and so, over a period of time, they absorb a much greater dose of radiation than a patient does in one visit. For the patient, the benefit of having an X-ray outweighs the harm done by it.

Q4 a) It absorbs some of the UV rays from the Sun.
b) CFCs (chlorofluorocarbons)

Pages 28-29 — Uses of Waves

Q1 a) It would take a very strong signal to transmit straight to the satellite, and this could be dangerous (especially as mobile phones are held right next to your head). Transmitting only as far as a nearby transmitter requires a much less powerful signal, and so is less dangerous.
b) i) Carwyn's phone is no longer in line of sight with a transmitter. The tall buildings have blocked the path of the microwaves, and the microwaves can't diffract around the buildings.
ii) The transmitter needs to be in line of sight, and putting it on a hill is the easiest way to do that.

Q2 a) Microwaves are absorbed by water in the curry. They make the water molecules vibrate, increasing their heat energy. The heat energy is conducted to other parts of the curry, heating it up.
b) Microwaves only penetrate a couple of centimetres into the curry, so they only heat up the outer bit — it then takes time for the heat from the outside to be conducted to the middle. If the food isn't left long enough, the middle can be underdone. Stirring would have helped mix hot and cold bits, which would have reduced the time taken for the temperature to even out.

Q3 soft tissue, absorbed, bone, lead

Q4 a) They have to reflect the laser light that is shone onto them.
b) The surface of a CD has a series of high and low areas (called lands and pits), which reflect the laser light differently. As the CD spins and the laser moves across the surface of the CD, differences in the way pits and lands reflect the laser light are detected. They are converted first into an electrical signal, and then into sounds.

Q5 night vision camera
(It detects infrared radiation emitted by hot objects.)

Q6 a) E.g. the sex of the baby, whether the baby is suffering from Down's syndrome.
b) X-rays would be dangerous for the foetus.

Q7 a) True
b) True
c) False — it could be rewritten as: Iris scanners use **visible light** to form the image of a person's iris.

Page 30 — Analogue and Digital Signals

Q1 weaken, amplified, interference, noise, analogue

Q2 E.g.

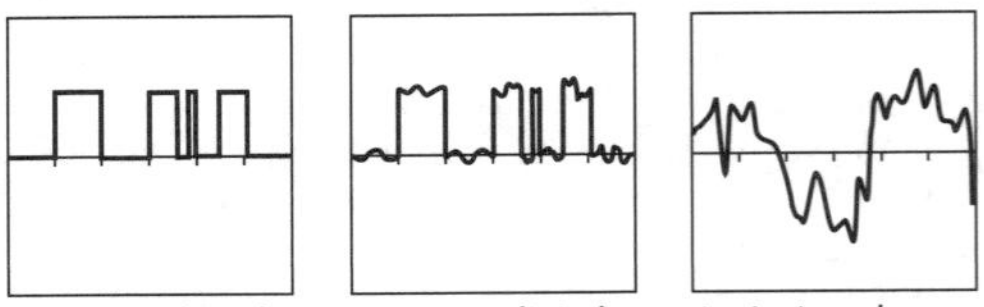

'clean' digital signal | 'noisy' digital signal | 'noisy' analogue signal

Q3 a) Computers process digital information only. Analogue signals would first have to be converted to digital ones.
b) The 'on' and 'off' phases of a digital signal can usually be recognised as 'on' and 'off' even when the signal is noisy, and noise can be removed when the signal is boosted.
c) E.g. more information can be sent at one time / digital signals are easier to encrypt.
Other answers are possible.

Section Three — Radioactivity and Space

Q4 The signal on the CD is a series of 'on' or 'off' signals and so is a pulsed digital signal. The record needle stays in the groove and would give a continuous signal as it moves from side to side. This is an analogue signal.

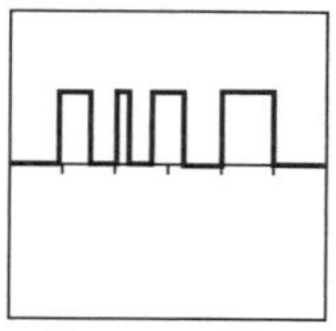

Compact Disc

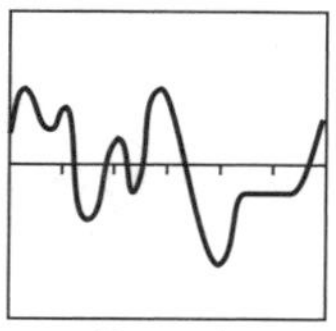

Record

Page 31 — Seismic Waves

Q1

Layer	Name	Solid or liquid
A	inner core	Solid
B	mantle	Solid
C	outer core	Liquid
D	crust	Solid

Q2 a) P waves
b) P waves
c) S waves (since S waves cannot travel through a liquid).
d) P waves (since S waves don't travel across the mantle-core boundary, where the properties change very quickly, and which cause the sudden change in direction of the P waves).
Q3 a) **B** and **C** should be circled
b) **A** — only P waves can travel through the core
D — they travel faster because it is solid
Q4 a) They change direction and speed as the nature of the material (e.g. the density) of the Earth changes. This is refraction.
b) i) S waves don't reach the other side.
ii) This tells us that the core must be liquid.

Section Three — Radioactivity and Space

Pages 32-33 — Radioactivity

Q1 protons, neutrons, radioactive, nuclei, radiation, element
Q2 Carbon 14 has two more neutrons than carbon 12. This makes it unstable.
Q3 a) True
b) False
c) False
Q4

Radiation Type	Ionising power weak/moderate/strong	Charge positive/-none/negative	Relative mass no mass/small/large	Penetrating power low/moderate/high	Relative speed slow/fast/very fast
alpha	strong	positive	large	low	slow
beta	moderate	negative	small	moderate	fast
gamma	weak	none	no mass	high	very fast

Q5 a) False
b) True
c) True
d) False
Q6 a) source A — gamma
source B — alpha
source C — beta
b) Gamma radiation has no electric charge.
c) a magnetic field
Q7 Gamma rays are more penetrating than alpha particles. This means they are less likely to hit an atom and knock electrons off it.

Page 34 — Background Radiation

Q1 The first two statements are true.
Q2 Any five from: the air, rocks, food, building materials, space/the Sun/cosmic rays, fallout from nuclear explosions/accidents, nuclear waste, medical activity/X-rays/radiotherapy/isotope tracing, other industrial uses of radioactive materials and X-rays.
Q3 Peter is correct to say that both materials are radioactive, but he is not correct to say that Material B is twice as radioactive as Material A. He has not taken account of background radiation, which should be subtracted from all experimental readings.
Q4 a) Because radon gas is radioactive and can cause cancer.
b) Radon gas comes from certain rocks (such as granite) which contain unstable isotopes. Some places have more of these rocks than others.
c) E.g. all new houses in problem areas should have good ventilation systems which remove radon gas.

Page 35 — Half-Life

Q1 a) Half-life is the time taken for the count rate to halve (e.g. from 1200 cpm to 600 cpm). This is about **80 minutes**.
b) After 240 minutes, the count rate was **150 cpm** (by reading from the graph or by calculating 1200 ÷ 8).
c) After 1 half-life, one half are still unstable.
After 2 half-lives, one quarter are still unstable.
After 3 half-lives, one eighth are still unstable.
After 4 half-lives, one sixteenth will be unstable.

So after 5 half-lives, $\frac{1}{32}$ of the atoms will be unstable.

d) Reading from the graph, approximately **285 mins**.
Q2 a) 6 × 60 = 360 seconds. 360 ÷ 40 = 9 half-lives.

After 9 half-lives, $\frac{1}{2^9} = \frac{1}{512}$ will still be radioactive.

b) i) $8000 \times \frac{1}{512} \approx$ **16** cpm.

ii) After 9 half-lives (6 minutes), the count rate is 16, so only one more half-life would be needed for the count to fall below 10 (to 8). So it would take **7 whole minutes**.

Page 36 — Dangers from Nuclear Radiation

Q1 E.g. He isn't wearing protective gloves. He isn't using tongs to hold the sample. He is pointing the sample directly in the face of the other scientist.
Q2 a) Beta and gamma.
b) i) alpha radiation
ii) It is highly ionising and can kill or damage the cells of our body. Cells which are damaged can mutate and divide uncontrollably, leading to cancer.
Q3 a) E.g. by using remote-controlled machinery, e.g. a robot arm / the radioactive material could be put in a lead-lined box / the workers could wear lead-lined suits.
b) E.g. by thick walls made of concrete or with lead screens.

Page 37 — Uses of Nuclear Radiation

Q1
1. The radioactive source emits alpha particles.
2. The air between the electrodes is ionised by the alpha particles.
3. A current flows between the electrodes — the alarm stays off.
4. A fire starts and smoke particles absorb the alpha radiation.
5. The circuit is broken so no current flows.
6. The alarm sounds.

Section Three — Radioactivity and Space

Q2 Beta radiation is used because it can pass through paper, but the amount of radiation which passes through will depend on the thickness of the paper. (Alpha would not pass through at all and gamma would virtually always pass through.)

Q3 a) A gamma-emitter with a long half-life is used. Gamma radiation is needed because it is not stopped by air or metal parts of the instruments and can kill the cells of living organisms (e.g. bacteria) on the instruments. A long half-life is needed because the sterilising machine will be in use over many years and replacing the source frequently would be inconvenient.

b) Lead is used to prevent the operator and anyone near the machine from getting too high a dose of radiation.

c) It kills or damages any living cells in the fruit — including the ones in insects and in microbes which make the fruit decay.

Q4 a) Gamma radiation would pass easily through any cracked areas in the turbine blade but would be partially absorbed by the uncracked areas. So cracks would show up as high gamma energy at the detector.

b) The hammer method could break a cracked blade (that could otherwise be repaired).

Page 38 — Radioactive Dating

Q1 a) The proportion of carbon-14 starts to decrease (it decays and isn't replaced by more carbon-14).

b) After 5730 years, you would expect the number of atoms of carbon-14 in a sample to have halved.

Q2 a) After 1 half-life, there would be 1 part in 20 000 000 C-14. After 2 half-lives, there would be 1 part in 40 000 000. After 3 half-lives, there would be 1 part in 80 000 000. So the strap is 3 half-lives old. The strap is 3 × 5730 = **approximately 17 200 years old**.

b) E.g. any two of: the sample may have been contaminated / there could have been a measuring error / the level of C-14 in the atmosphere hasn't stayed constant.

Q3 3700 BCE is about 1 C-14 half-life ago, so you would expect there to be about 1 part in 20 000 000 C-14.

Q4 If the tusk contains 1 part in 15 000 000 C-14, it is very likely to be less than one half-life old (after one half-life, it would contain about 1 part in 20 000 000). That makes the tusk less than 5730 years old, so it is unlikely to be genuine.

Q5 The ratio 1:1 means that 50% of the original uranium is still uranium, and the other 50% is lead. This would happen after 1 half-life.
So the meteorite is **4.5 billion years old**.

Page 39 — The Solar System

Q1

Object	Mars	Jupiter	Asteroids	Venus	Saturn	Neptune	Earth	Mercury	Uranus
number	4	6	5	2	7	9	3	1	8

Q2 E.g. the planets do not give out their own light / the planets only reflect light / the planets are much smaller than the stars / the planets are much closer than the stars.

Q3 a) an ellipse / elliptical

b) i) C

ii) A

c) The force of the Sun's gravity accelerates the comet towards the Sun. The force is greater, the closer the comet is to the Sun.

d) i) Dust and ice.

ii) The ice in the comet melts as it approaches the Sun leaving a bright trail of gas and debris.

Q4 To find out if any will strike the Earth, in enough time to plan action to deal with them.

Page 40 — Magnetic Fields and Solar Flares

Q1 a) b) c)

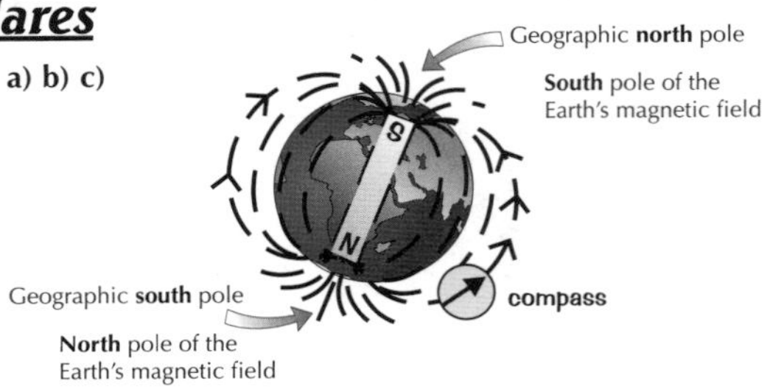

Q2 a) X-rays and gamma rays.

b) E.g. one of: they create gamma rays / they ionise the gases in the atmosphere.

c) It deflects them away.

Q3 They give off massive clouds of charged particles which can reach the Earth.

Q4 a) Polar lights are shifting 'curtains of light' in the sky.

b) Charged particles are deflected by the Earth's magnetic field and spiral down near the magnetic poles. Some of the particles' energy is transferred to particles in the atmosphere, causing them to emit light.

Page 41 — Beyond the Solar System

Q1 C

Q2 a) It is the distance travelled in one year by light travelling in a vacuum.

b) $3 \times 10^8 \times 24 \times 60 \times 60 \times 365.25 \div 1000 =$
$\mathbf{9.47 \times 10^{12}}$ **km** (to 3 s.f.)

c) Assuming that we are approximately 25 000 light years from the centre of the galaxy, then
$25\,000 \times 9.47 \times 10^{12} = 2.5 \times 10^4 \times 9.47 \times 10^{12} =$
$\mathbf{23.675 \times 10^{16} = 2.37 \times 10^{17}}$ **km**.

Q3 a) Black holes have extremely strong gravitational fields which attract everything, even light. Nothing — not even light — can escape from the region of the black hole so it appears black.

b) E.g. they observe X-rays emitted by hot gases from other stars as they spiral into the black hole.

Page 42 — The Life Cycle of Stars

Q1 a) heat (from thermonuclear fusion)

b) gravity

c) The force pulling the star inwards and the force pushing it outwards are equal, so they balance and cancel out.

d) a main sequence star

Q2 a) Gravitational attraction pulls the material together.

b) The energy is released when hydrogen nuclei fuse together to form helium nuclei / from thermonuclear fusion.

Q3 a) Its core runs out of hydrogen.

b) Its surface is cooler than a main sequence star's surface.

Q4 white dwarf, black dwarf, supernova, neutron star, black holes

Q5 E.g. It glows brightly again as it undergoes more fusion reactions and forms heavier elements. It expands and contracts several times before eventually exploding in a supernova.

Page 43 — The Origins of the Universe

Q1 a) matter/energy, energy/matter, explosion, expand, age, expansion.

b) Because we do not know how much the rate of expansion has changed since the Big Bang.

Section Four — Forces and Energy

Q2 E.g. Light from other galaxies is red-shifted — all the frequencies are lower in the spectrum than is the case for similar objects nearby. This tells us that the galaxies are moving away from us. Also, the further away the galaxy, the greater the red-shift, so more distant galaxies must be moving away faster than nearer ones, i.e. the whole Universe must be expanding. The low frequency radiation coming from all parts of the Universe — cosmic background radiation — tells us that the Universe has expanded and cooled.

Q3 a) How fast galaxies are moving apart and the total mass in the Universe.

b) Dark matter is matter that appears to be invisible. Scientists can only detect it because it affects the movement of things we can see.

Q4 a) In a big crunch.

b) endless expansion

Page 44 — Exploring the Solar System

Q1 E.g. any four of: supplying sufficient food, water, and oxygen / temperature control / waste management / stress / muscle wastage / boredom / carrying sufficient fuel for lift off and manoeuvres.

Q2 a) E.g. any two from: they're cheaper than manned probes / they can withstand conditions (such as dangerous radiation levels) that would kill people / there's no need to carry food, etc. / there's more payload available for instruments / they can accelerate faster without risk of the g-force harming the crew /there's no risk of astronauts losing their lives.

b) E.g. they cannot think for themselves / they cannot self-repair so well.

c) i) E.g. it could collect data on temperature, magnetism, gravity, radiation, atmospheric composition, information about the planet's surface — it could collect and analyse samples of dust, rocks etc., take photographs, search for particular features.

ii) E.g. If the probe deviates even slightly from its planned descent it may not slow down enough, so it may be damaged by overheating during descent or by crash-landing. Or it may land on an unsuitable (e.g. very rocky) part of the surface, also causing damage on impact.

Pages 45-46 — Looking into Space

Q1 Patrick would probably be able to see stars more clearly in the countryside because there would be less light/air pollution.

Q2 a) By using a very big telescope to collect as much light as possible, or by using a number of telescopes connected together. (Or other sensible answers.)

b) By increasing the size of the mirrors/lenses of the telescope. The more light they collect the more detailed the image will be. So again, the bigger the telescope the better the image.
For both a) and b), the position of the telescope is important — on top of a hill, away from pollution etc.

Q3 a) The Hubble Telescope is not affected by the Earth's atmosphere and any pollution it contains. It is also not affected by light pollution from streetlamps, etc.

b) E.g. any three from: space telescopes are much more expensive to make than most terrestrial telescopes / they need to be put into orbit by a rocket — this is also expensive / they are very difficult to adjust or repair if things go wrong / they may be damaged by the vibrations of the rocket launch, so they need to be made very robustly yet with lightweight materials — this is quite difficult.

Q4 Not all the objects and events in space can be seen using optical telescopes (which only detect visible light). Stars and galaxies emit all the different types of EM radiation, and the type of radiation they emit may change e.g. during the different parts of a star's life cycle. Using different telescopes to gather different types of radiation allows astronomers to observe what's happening even if no visible light is emitted. Also, clouds of dust, etc. can block visible light but can often be seen through with other types of radiation.

Q5 a) Because radio waves have very long wavelengths, and the longer the wave, the bigger the telescope you need to get the same level of detail.

b) Infrared — these are longer waves than UV.

Q6 The Earth's atmosphere absorbs X-rays, so an X-ray telescope on Earth would not be able to 'see' anything.

Section Four — Forces and Energy

Page 47 — Velocity and Acceleration

Q1 Speed $= \frac{\text{distance}}{\text{time}}$, so distance = speed × time =
$3 \times 10^8 \times 1.3 = 390\ 000\ 000$ m. Dividing by 1000 gives **390 000 km** (3.9×10^5 km).

Q2 a) Since the egg was dropped from rest, its change in speed is 80 m/s. Putting the numbers into the formula you get
acceleration $= \frac{\text{change in velocity}}{\text{time}} = \frac{80}{8} = \mathbf{10\ m/s^2}$.

b) Now rearrange the formula to get
time $= \frac{\text{change in velocity}}{\text{acceleration}} = \frac{40}{10} = \mathbf{4\ s}$.

Q3 First work out how fast the train is going in m/s —
12 km × 1000 = 12 000 m, 20 mins × 60 = 1200 s.
Speed $= \frac{\text{distance}}{\text{time}} = \frac{12\ 000}{1200} = 10$ m/s.
The speed rules out **A** and **C**.
The train is travelling east so **E** is wrong.
Velocity should have a direction so you can discount **B**.
So the answer is **D**. The train's average speed is 10 m/s.

Q4 You need to find the total time it would take for each of the takeaways to reach the house.
Ludo's Pizza:
Time for delivery $= \frac{\text{distance}}{\text{speed}} = \frac{6.5}{30} = 0.217$ hours.
Time taken to cook the food is 0.25 hours, so the total time is 0.47 hours.
Moonlight Indian Takeaway:
Time for delivery $= \frac{\text{distance}}{\text{speed}} = \frac{4}{40} = 0.1$ hours.
Time taken to cook the food is 0.5 hours, so the total time is 0.6 hours.
So they should order from **Ludo's Pizza**.

Q5 Rearranging the formula for acceleration you get:
change in velocity = acceleration × time = 2 × 4 = 8 m/s. Change in velocity = final velocity – initial velocity, so initial velocity = final velocity – change in velocity = 24 – 8 = **16 m/s**.

Page 48 — D-T and V-T Graphs

Q1 a) 180 s (or 3 mins)

b) Speed $= \frac{\text{distance}}{\text{time}} = \frac{450}{180} = \mathbf{2.5\ m/s}$.

Section Four — Forces and Energy

c) He runs there in half the time it took him to walk there — 90 s. See graph:

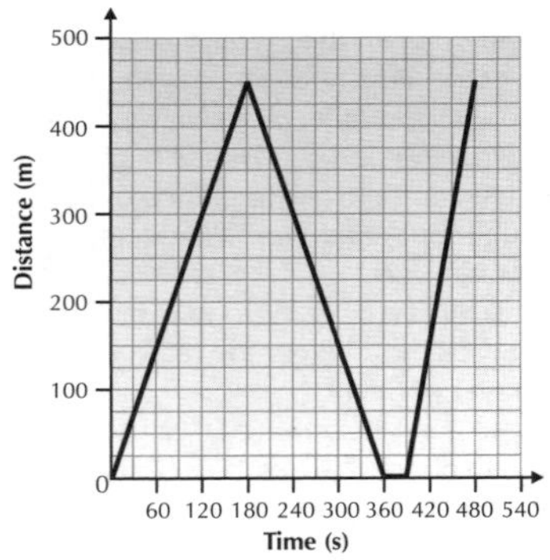

Q2 The graph shows that the motorist accelerates for about 1.5 seconds, then travels at a constant speed. So the gradient of the graph between 1.5 s and 3.0 s will give you the speed. Gradient = vertical change ÷ horizontal change = (72 – 18) ÷ (3.0 – 1.5) = 54 ÷ 1.5 = 36 m/s — i.e. she was exceeding the speed limit.
So the motorist wasn't telling the truth.

Q3 The distance the motorist travels before stopping is equal to the area under the graph. To find it, split the graph into a rectangle and a triangle. Area of the rectangle = base × height = 0.75 × 12 = 9 m. Area of the triangle = half × base × height. 0.5 × 2.5 × 12 = 15 m. Total distance = 9 m + 15 m = 24 m. He didn't hit the puppy.

Page 49 — Mass, Weight and Gravity

Q1 The fourth statement should be ticked.

Q2 a) Professor White's reasoning is incorrect. The mass of the rocket will be the same on any planet — it's the weight that will change.

b) $\text{Mass} = \frac{\text{weight}}{\text{gravity}}$, and gravity on Earth is 10 m/s², so the extinguisher must have a mass of 5 kg. $\frac{1.9\text{ kg}}{5\text{ kg}} = 0.38.$

The balance reads 38% of the true mass, so the gravitational field strength on Mars is 38% of that on Earth. 10 m/s² × 38% = **3.8 m/s²**.

Q3 Plot the points and draw a line of best fit. It will go through the origin, since a mass of 0 kg will have no weight.

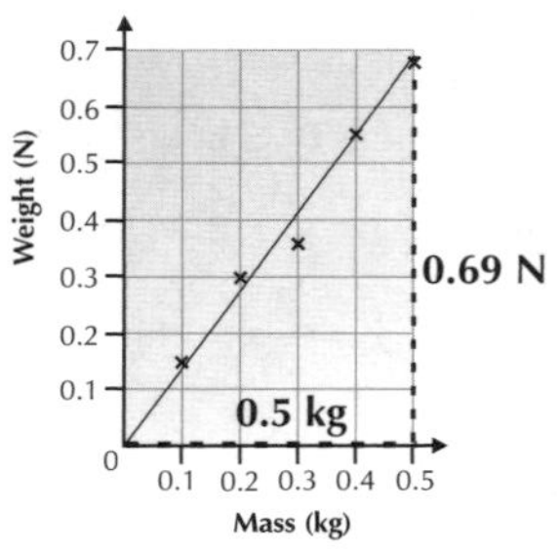

Gravitational field strength = $\frac{\text{weight}}{\text{mass}}$, so find the gradient of the line to find the gravity on Europa.

$$\text{Gradient} = \frac{\text{rise}}{\text{tread}} = \frac{0.69\text{ N}}{0.5\text{ kg}} = \mathbf{1.38\ N/kg}.$$

Pages 50-51 — The Three Laws of Motion

Q1 balanced, stationary, constant /
resultant, accelerates, force, proportional, inversely proportional /
opposite reaction.

Q2 The second statement should be ticked.

Q3 If there is acceleration in any direction, the forces can't be balanced:

a) Unbalanced — the ball is slowing down, which is negative acceleration.

b) Unbalanced — motion in a circle means constantly changing direction, which requires acceleration.

c) Unbalanced — the vase will be accelerating due to gravity.

d) Unbalanced — as **b)**.

e) Balanced — without air resistance or gravity there will be no acceleration — the bag will continue travelling in the direction it was ejected at the speed it was given when ejected.

Q4 Force = Mass × Acceleration.
Disraeli 9000: 800 kg × 5 m/s² = 4000 N
Palmerston 6i: 1560 kg × 0.7 m/s² = 1092 N
Heath TT: 950 kg × 3 m/s² = 2850 N
Asquith 380: 790 kg × 2 m/s² = 1580 N
So the correct order is: **Palmerston 6i**, **Asquith 380**, **Heath TT**, **Disraeli 9000**.

Q5 a) The force of the engine is 110 kg × 2.80 m/s² = 308 N.

b) $$\text{Mass} = \frac{\text{Force}}{\text{Acceleration}} = \frac{308\text{ N}}{1.71\text{ m/s}^2} = \mathbf{180.1\,kg}.$$

Q6 Since the probe came back, it must have changed direction, which requires acceleration. Acceleration requires a force, so some fuel must have been burnt. (Although it's possible that the change in direction could be made by using the gravity of a planet or other body in space.)

Q7 Using F = ma, the resultant force on the mass must be 1 kg × 0.25 m/s² = 0.25 N.
Resultant force = force on the newton-meter – force of friction (they act in opposite directions).
0.25 N = 0.4 N – force of friction, so force of friction = 0.4 N – 0.25 N = **0.15 N**.

Q8 A

Page 52 — Friction Forces and Terminal Speed

Q1 greater, accelerates, increase, balances, constant, greater, decelerates, decrease, balances, constant

Q2 All the boxes except 'carrying less cargo' should be ticked.

Q3 a) Paola is **wrong** because although gravity (the accelerating force per unit mass) is the same for both objects, air resistance will affect them differently because they have different shapes.

b) Guiseppe is **right** because drag will be greater for the feather compared to its weight, so drag will balance its weight sooner. The hammer will continue to accelerate for longer than the feather.

Q4 No, Mavis can't draw any conclusions.
The terminal velocity depends not only on drag (which is determined by the size, shape and smoothness of the object) but on the weight of the object, and the weights of the balls will be different.

Page 53 — Stopping Distances

Q1 a) How far a car travels once the brakes are applied.

b) i) Thinking distance = **speed** × **reaction time**. (Or the other way round.)

ii) Stopping distance = **thinking** distance + **braking** distance. (Or the other way round.)

Section Four — Forces and Energy

Q2

Thinking Distance	Braking Distance
Tiredness	Road surface
Alcohol	Tyres
Speed	Weather
	Brakes
	Speed
	Load

Q3 The third box should be ticked — thinking distance will double and braking distance will more than double.

Q4 The friction between the brake discs and pads will be reduced if they are covered in water. This means the braking force will be reduced and the car will take longer to stop (i.e. the braking distance increases).

Page 54 — Momentum and Collisions

Q1 Truck A's momentum = 30 m/s × 3000 kg = 90 000 kg m/s.
Truck B's momentum = 10 m/s × 4500 kg = 45 000 kg m/s.
Truck C's momentum = 20 m/s × 4000 kg = 80 000 kg m/s.
Truck D's momentum = 15 m/s × 3500 kg = 52 500 kg m/s.
So the correct order is: **B, D, C, A**.

Q2 $\text{Momentum}_{\text{before}} = 60 \text{ kg} \times 5 \text{ m/s} = 300 \text{ kg m/s}$
$\text{Momentum}_{\text{before}} = \text{momentum}_{\text{after}}$
so, $300 \text{ kg m/s} = m_{(\text{skater + bag})} \times 4.8 \text{ m/s}$
so, $m_{(\text{skater + bag})} = 300 \div 4.8 = 62.5 \text{ kg}$
so, the mass of the bag = 62.5 – 60 = **2.5 kg**.

Q3 The **second** and **third** statements should be ticked.

Q4 a) Momentum of car = 750 kg × 30 m/s = 22 500 kg m/s. When the car has stopped its momentum = 0 kg m/s. So the change in momentum is 22 500 kg m/s. Average force = change in momentum ÷ time = 22 500 kg m/s ÷ 1.2 s = **18 750 N**

b) Wearing slightly stretchy seat belts means that the occupants will take slightly longer (than 1.2 seconds) to stop moving and the force exerted on their bodies will be lower (than 18 750 N).

Page 55 — Car Safety

Q1 a) kinetic energy

b) The kinetic energy is mainly converted to heat in the brakes (and a little bit of sound).

Q2 a) A smaller deceleration means a smaller force acting on the passengers, reducing the risk of injury.

b) i) Parts of the car crumple up to slow the car down more gradually.

ii) The air bag is soft, so it slows down the passengers over a longer time.

Q3 safety, interact, crashes, power, control, skidding, lock, steering

Q4 The crash barrier crumples to slow the car down gradually and absorb some of the energy of the impact.

Page 56 — Work and Potential Energy

Q1 a) Work involves the transfer of **energy**.

b) To do work a **force** acts over a **distance**.

c) Work is measured in **joules**.

Q2 a) True

b) True

c) False

d) True

Q3 a) Work done = force × distance = 1200 N × 8 m = **9600 J**

b) From the chemical energy in its food.

c) Heat energy (because of friction between the donkey's feet and the surface of the track) and some sound energy.

Q4 a) Gravity / his weight.

b) It is transferred into kinetic energy — in his moving legs and arms — which is then transferred into potential energy — as he gains height. (Some of the energy supplied is also wasted as heat and sound.)

c) Work done = force × distance moved = 600 N × 2 m = **1200 J**

d) 15 kJ = 15 000 J = 600 N × distance
so, distance = 15 000 ÷ 600 = 25 m
Each step is 0.2 m high, so the number of rungs Ben must climb is 25 ÷ 0.2 = **125 rungs**.

Page 57 — Kinetic Energy

Q1 $\text{K.E.} = \frac{1}{2}mv^2 = \frac{1}{2} \times 200 \times (9)^2 = 0.5 \times 200 \times 81 = \mathbf{8100\ J}$

Q2 $9 \text{ J} = \frac{1}{2} \times m \times (20)^2 = \frac{1}{2} \times m \times 400$
so, $m = (9 \times 2) \div 400 = \mathbf{0.045\ kg}$

Q3 $\text{K.E.} = 2000 \text{ J} = \frac{1}{2} \times 0.004 \text{ kg} \times v^2 = 0.002 \times v^2$,
so rearranging gives:
$v = \sqrt{2000 \div 0.002} = \sqrt{1\ 000\ 000} = \mathbf{1000\ m/s}$.

Q4 Kinetic energy is proportional to velocity^2 so if the speed increases to 5/3 (50/30) of its original value, the distance needed to stop will be approximately 25/9 its original value — just under 3 times. 14 × 25 ÷ 9 ≈ 39 m.

Q5 a) Work done against gravity is mass × g × height = 70 × 10 × 20 = **14 000 J**.

b) The gravitational potential energy the skier gained is converted into kinetic energy when she skis down the slope.
So, $\text{K.E.} = 14\ 000 \text{ J} = \frac{1}{2}mv^2 = \frac{1}{2} \times 70 \times v^2$
so rearranging gives $v = \sqrt{14\ 000 \div 35} = \sqrt{400}$ = **20 m/s**.

Page 58 — Roller Coasters

Q1 a) A — maximum P.E.
B — P.E. is being converted to K.E.
C — minimum P.E., maximum K.E.
D — K.E. is being converted to P.E.

b) i) Decrease in K.E. = increase in K.E.
so you would expect K.E. = 300 ÷ 2 = **150 kJ**

ii) There is friction between the carriage and the track, so some of the P.E. is converted into heat.

c) No. (Assuming there's no friction) all things move with the same acceleration under gravity, so the mass of the carriage makes no difference.

Q2 a) W = m × g = 1500 × 15 = **22 500 N** (or 22.5 kN)

b) i) P.E. = m × g × h = 1500 × 15 × 25 = **562 500 J** (or 562.5 kJ)

ii) 562 500 J (or 562.5 kJ)

c) i) change in P.E. = m × g × change in h
= 1500 × 15 × (25 – 7) = **405 000 J** (or 405 kJ)

ii) $\text{K.E.} = 405\ 000 \text{ J} = \frac{1}{2}mv^2 = \frac{1}{2} \times 1500 \times v^2$
so, $v^2 = (405\ 000 \times 2) \div 1500 = 540$
v = 23.2 m/s

Page 59 — Power

Q1 a) 10 minutes = 10 × 60 = 600 seconds
energy = power × time = 150 × 600 = **90 000 J** (or 90 kJ)

b) Fuel used = 90 kJ ÷ 30 kJ/ml = **3 ml**

c) Power = energy ÷ time = 120 000 ÷ 600 = **200 W**

Q2 a) $\text{Final K.E.} = \frac{1}{2}mv^2 = \frac{1}{2} \times (60 + 5) \times 8^2 = 2080 \text{ J}$
power = energy ÷ time = 2080 ÷ 6 = **346.7 W**

b) P.E. = m × g × h = 60 × 10 × 5 = 3000 J
power = energy ÷ time = 3000 ÷ 4 = **750 W**

Q3 a) sprint 4 (because he slipped)

b) E.g. Calculate the power for each start, e.g., for sprint 1 power = $(1/2 \times 70 \times 8^2) / 3.2 = 700$ W.
Then average these powers. 2804 ÷ 4 = **701 W**.

Section Five — Electricity

Page 60 — Fuels for Cars

Q1 a) non-renewable
b) E.g. acid rain, global warming.
c) E.g. hydrogen, bio-diesel, liquid petroleum gas (LPG), alcohol, etc.

Q2 a) Electric motors don't emit harmful gases.
b) The batteries used to run the electric motor can only provide a limited amount of electricity. The car can only go a certain distance before they have to be recharged.
c) Yes. The energy used to charge the batteries will probably come from the burning of fossil fuels, which does have a significant impact on the environment (and even energy generation from renewable sources usually has some environmental impact).

Q3 The car uses 3.4 l every 100 km. The journey is 2.5 times 100 km, so the car will use 2.5 × 3.4 = **8.5 l**.

Q4 a) i) Roof racks **increase** the fuel consumption of a moving car because they make the car less streamlined, so more work has to be done by the engine in overcoming air resistance. (They also increase the mass of the car, so more work needs to be done by the engine to move the car.)
ii) Open windows **increase** fuel consumption of a moving car by making it less streamlined. More work will need to be done to overcome the increase in air resistance.
b) Cars work more efficiently at some speeds than others. Most cars are usually most efficient at around 50 mph. At higher speeds, fuel consumption increases very rapidly the faster you go.

Section Five — Electricity

Pages 61-62 — Static Electricity

Q1 static, insulating, friction, electrons, positive / negative, negative / positive

Q2 circled: positive and negative, negative and positive
underlined: positive and positive, negative and negative

Q3 a) Because rubber is an insulating material (and flexible).
b) So that electrons can move and charge can be transferred to the dome.
c) As Nadia becomes charged, so does her hair. Because each strand of hair has the same charge, the strands repel each other.

Q4 Lisa: Because they rub against each other, which scrapes off electrons, causing static charge. The charge can't move (the clothes are insulators), so charge builds up throughout the day.
Sara: No. Charging mainly happens with synthetic (man-made) materials. Cotton is a natural material.
Tim: The sound is caused by small sparks as the charges on the shirt are discharged.

Q5 sparks, fuel, explosion, earthed, grain chutes / paper rollers, paper rollers / grain chutes

Q6 Raindrops and ice bump together... and electrons move between them.
The bottoms of the clouds become negatively charged... because they gain extra electrons.
As the charge increases... the voltage gets higher and higher.
If the voltage gets big enough... there is a huge spark (a flash of lightning).

Page 63 — Uses of Static Electricity

Q1 shock, defibrillator, paddles, shock, insulated

Q2 a) This gives the smoke particles a negative charge.
b) To attract the smoke particles.
c) The smoke is negatively charged and the plates are positively charged, so they are attracted to each other.

Q3 a) Light shining on the image plate causes the charge to leak away.
b) The powder is negatively charged, so is attracted by the positively charged image plate.
c) The paper wouldn't attract the black powder, so the page would be blank.

Page 64 — Circuits — The Basics

Q1 a) current
b) voltage, force
c) more
d) resistance, less

Q2

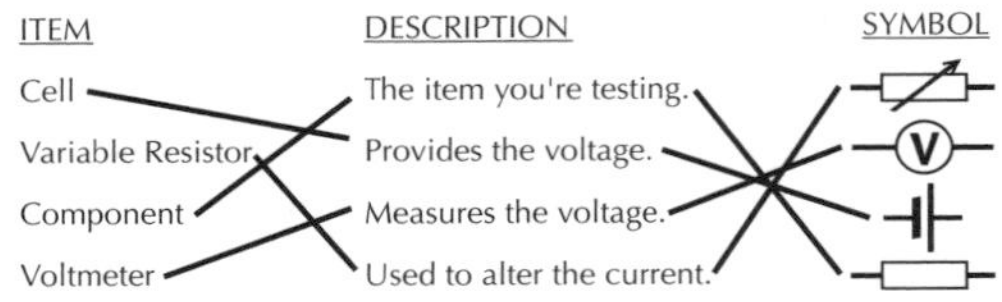

Q3 a) i) ampere / amp
ii) volt
iii) ohm
b) E.g. any two from: increase the resistance of the variable resistor / insert a component of higher resistance / reduce the voltage from the battery.

Q4 a) True
b) False. An ammeter should be connected in series with a component / A voltmeter should be connected in parallel with a component.
c) True
d) False. A voltmeter should be connected in parallel with a component / An ammeter should be connected in series with a component.

Page 65 — Resistance and Devices

Q1
1. battery
2. ammeter
3. LDR / light-dependent resistor
4. LED / light-emitting diode

Q2 a)

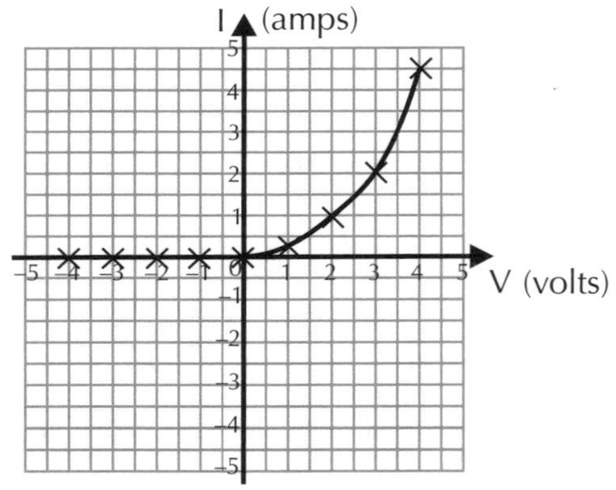

b) When V = 3, I = 2.
Using V = IR, R = V ÷ I = 3 ÷ 2 = **1.5 Ω**
c) diode

Page 66 — Measuring AC

Q1 volts, alternating, AC, direction, changing, frequency, hertz

Q2 a) Cathode Ray Oscilloscope
b) Voltage and time (or another voltage).
c) Gain and timebase

Q3 a) C
b) B
c) A

Q4 a) 2 volts
b) 4 × 10 ms = **40 ms** or **0.04 s**
c) Frequency = 1 ÷ 0.04 = **25 Hz**

Section Six — Mechanics

Page 67 — Series Circuits

Q1 Same everywhere in the circuit — Current.
Shared out between the components — Total potential difference.
The sum of the resistances — Total resistance.
Can be different for each component — Potential difference.

Q2 a) 2 V + 2 V + 2 V = **6 V**
b) V = I x R, so total R = total V ÷ total I = 6 ÷ 0.5 = **12 Ω**
c) R_3 = total resistance – R_1 – R_2 = 12 – 2 – 4 = **6 Ω**
d) V = I x R = 0.5 x 4 = **2 V**

Q3 a) The lamps get dimmer as more are added because the voltage is shared out between the lamps.
b) The current gets smaller as more lamps are added. Each lamp adds more resistance which means less current.

Page 68 — Parallel Circuits

Q1 a) False
b) True
c) False
d) True

Q2 a) Nothing, because each lamp gets its voltage from the battery separately.
b) Nothing.
(The answers above assume that the internal resistance of the cell is ignored — in practice the current would decrease a little as lamps were added.)

Q3 a) i) I = V ÷ R = 12 ÷ 2 = **6 A**
ii) I = V ÷ R = 12 ÷ 4 = **3 A**
b) i) **12 V**
ii) **12 V**
c) R = V ÷ I = 12 ÷ 2 = **6 Ω**
d) $A_0 = A_2 + A_3$ = 3 A + 2 A = **5 A**

Page 69 — Fuses and Safe Plugs

Q1 a) Because these materials are electrical insulators.
b) These materials are electrical conductors, and are used for those parts that need to carry current.

Q2 a) insulation
b) live
c) neutral
d) green and yellow, earth
e) firmly, bare
f) outer

Q3

Description	Live	Neutral	Earth
Must always be connected	✓	✓	
Just for safety			✓
Electricity normally flows in and out of it	✓	✓	
Alternates between +ve and –ve voltage	✓		

Q4 a)
1. A fault develops and the earthed casing becomes connected to the live supply.
2. A large current now flows in through the live wire and out through the earth wire.
3. The surge in current causes the fuse wire to heat up.
4. The fuse blows.
5. The live supply is cut off.
6. Everything is now safe.

b) RCCBs can be reset, whereas if a fuse 'blows' it needs to be replaced / A RCCB breaks the circuit faster than a fuse.

Page 70 — Energy and Power in Circuits

Q1 how long, power rating, voltage/current, current/voltage, higher, current.

Q2 a) 1000 J, light, heat
b) 60 000 J, kinetic, heat, sound
c) 20 000 J, heat
d) 1 200 000 J, heat

Q3 a)

	Lamp A	Lamp B	Lamp C
Voltage (V)	12	3	230
Current (A)	2.5	4	0.1
Power (W)	30	12	23
Energy used in one minute (J)	1800	720	1380

b) A = 3 A, B = 5 A, C = 2 A.

Page 71 — Charge, Voltage and Energy Change

Q1 a) i) 20 × 60 = **1200 seconds**
ii) Q = I × t = 5 × 1200 = **6000 C**
b) 3 × 6000 = **18 000 J** (or **18 kJ**)

Q2

	Lamp A	Lamp B
Current through lamp (A)	2	4
Voltage drop across lamp (V)	3	2
Charge passing in 10 s (C)	20	40
Energy transformed in 10 s (J)	60	80

Q3 a) 4 × (7 × 60) = **1680 C**
b) 1680 × 9 = **15 120 J** (or 15.12 kJ)

Q4 a) Higher **current** means more coulombs of charge per second.
b) One ampere (amp) is the same as one **coulomb** per second.
c) One volt is the same as one joule per **coulomb**.

Section Six — Mechanics

Page 72 — Relative Speed and Velocity

Q1 a) 50 miles = 50 × 1609 = 80 450 m
1 hour = 60 × 60 = 3600 s
Speed = $\frac{\text{distance}}{\text{time}} = \frac{80\,450}{3600}$ = **22.3 m/s** which is about **22 m/s**.
b) Car moves 3 lots of 5 m (= 15 m) in 0.5 seconds.
Therefore speed of car = 15 / 0.5 =
30 m/s. So the car was breaking the speed limit.

Q2 scalar, temperature/speed, speed/temperature, direction, vector

Q3 350 + 278 = **628 mph**

Page 73 — Combining Velocities and Forces

Q1 a) 15 N right.
b) 80 N up (horizontal forces balance out).

Q2 a) 2.5 m/s due East (take East as positive then resultant velocity = 1 + 1.5).
b) 1 m/s due West (with East as positive the resultant velocity = 1 + –2 = –1).

Q3 a)

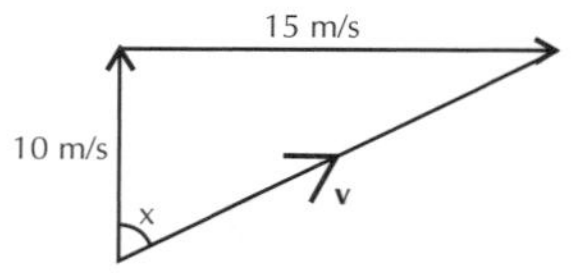

So the size of the velocity v is given by the hypotenuse of the triangle. Using Pythagoras' theorem:
$v^2 = 10^2 + 15^2 = 100 + 225 = 325$
so v = 18.0 m/s (to 3 s.f.).
Using trigonometry to find the angle x:
tan x = 15 ÷ 10 = 1.5 so x = 56.3° (to 3 s.f.).
So the velocity is **18 m/s** on a bearing of **56**°.

Section Six — Mechanics

b) Drawing a vector diagram to show how the velocities add up:

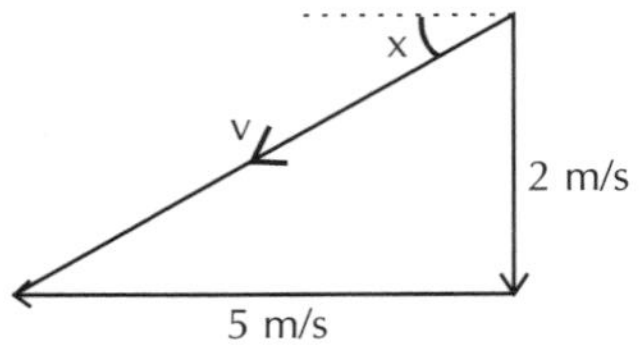
x
v
2 m/s
5 m/s

$v^2 = 2^2 + 5^2 = 4 + 25 = 29$
so v = 5.39 m/s (to 3 sf).
tan x = 2 ÷ 5 = 0.4 so x = 21.8° (to 3 sf).
So Emma's velocity is **5 m/s** on a bearing of **22°**.

Page 74 — Equations of Motion

Q1 a) i) displacement
ii) initial (starting) velocity
iii) final velocity
iv) time
v) acceleration

b) $s = ut + \frac{1}{2}at^2$

$s = \frac{(u + v)}{2}t$

$v = u + at$
$v^2 = u^2 + 2as$

Q2 a) $s = ut + ½ at^2$ so $s = (0 \times 20) + (½ \times 5 \times 20^2)$
$s = 0 + (½ \times 5 \times 400)$
s = **1000 m**.

b) $v^2 = u^2 + 2as$ so
$v^2 = 20^2 + (2 \times 1 \times 250)$
$v^2 = 400 + 500$
$v^2 = 900$
v = **30 m/s**.

c) Use the equation s = ½(u + v)t and rearrange it:
2s = (u + v) t
t = 2s ÷ (u + v)
t = (2 × 45) ÷ (3 + 15)
t = 90 ÷ 18
t = **5 s**.

d) Use the equation $s = ut + ½ at^2$ and rearrange it:
$½ at^2 = s - ut$
$a = 2(s - ut) \div t^2$
$a = 2 \times 100 \div 5^2$
t = **8 m/s²**.

Q3 v = u + at (where u = 0 and a = 2.5 m/s²)
v = 0 + (2.5 × 20) = **50 m/s**.

Q4 Taking upwards as positive u = 10 m/s,
a = –10 m/s².
At its maximum height — when it stops moving upwards and begins to move downwards again — its velocity is zero, so v = 0 m/s.
You need to find s so use $v^2 = u^2 + 2as$ and rearrange.
$0^2 = 10^2 + (2 \times -10 \times s)$
0 = 100 – 20s
20s = 100
s = 100 ÷ 20 = **5 m**.

Page 75 — Projectile Motion

Q1 gravity, trajectory, parabola
Q2 a) True
b) True
c) False
d) True
Q3 a) The droplets are equally spaced in the horizontal direction.
b) The vertical distance between one droplet and the next increases as the drops fall.

Q4 The following should be circled: a football kicked towards the goal, an orange rolling off a table, a cannonball fired from a cannon, a high jumper in flight.

Q5 a) The water has initial vertical velocity u = 0 m/s.
It has acceleration a = 10 m/s² (taking downwards as positive). Its displacement, s = 125 m.
To find t, use the equation $s = ut + ½ at^2$ and rearrange:
$125 = (0 \times t) + (½ \times 10 \times t^2)$
$125 = 5t^2$
$t^2 = 25$
so t = **5 s**.

b) The water has the same initial velocity as that of the plane (80 m/s horizontally). Ignoring air resistance, no forces act horizontally so the horizontal velocity is constant.
So distance travelled = speed × time = 80 × 5 = 400 m.
So the plane must release the water **400 m** before the fire.

Pages 76-78 — Turning Forces and Centre of Mass

Q1 a) force, moment, perpendicular, pivot
b) Nm (newton-metres)
Q2 a) M = F × d = 45 × 0.1 = **4.5 Nm**
b) i) B
ii) C
Q3 a) Yes. 45 N × 0.8 m = 36 Nm.
b) 30 ÷ 35 = 0.857 (to 3 sf). So Jez would need a crowbar at least **86 cm** long (although in practice it would have to be a bit longer so that he could grip it properly).

Q4 a)

The centre of mass must fall on this line

b) centre of mass, vertically below, perpendicular, moment.

Q5 a)

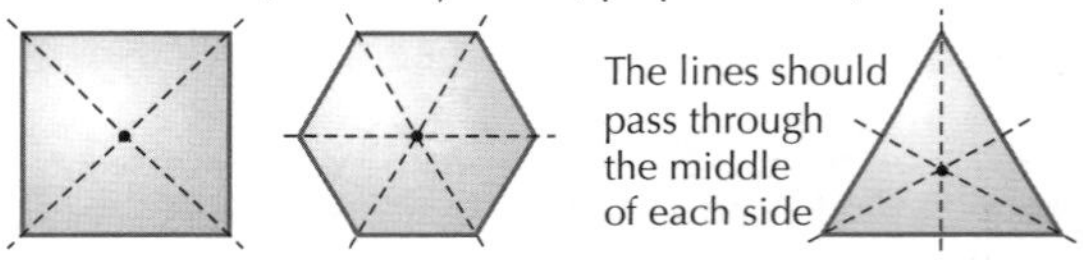
The lines should pass through the middle of each side

b) D

Q6 The weight of the pole acts at its centre of mass.
The centre of mass of the pole is 0.4 m from its end. M = F × d = 130 × 0.4 = **52 Nm**

Q7 a) Hang the plumb line from the same point as the piece of card. Draw a pencil line on the card along the plumb line. Hang the card in a different position and do the same thing again. Where the two lines cross is the centre of mass.

b) Preferred answer: Repeat the same steps for several pivot points to get multiple lines that will all cross at the centre of mass.
Other acceptable answers: make sure the card is not swaying when the lines are marked / is not moved by marking the lines / is not bent out of shape; make sure the line isn't too thick and is accurately placed.

Page 79 — Balanced Moments and Stability

Q1 a) M = F × d = 2 × 0.2 = **0.4 Nm** anticlockwise.
b) M = F × d = 5 × 0.16 = **0.8 Nm** anticlockwise.
c) Total anticlockwise moments = total clockwise moments.
0.4 Nm + 0.8 Nm = 8 N × distance
1.2 Nm = 8 N × distance
1.2 ÷ 8 = distance
distance = 0.15 m = **15 cm**

d) No. Since **all** the moments would be multiplied by 2, it would stay balanced.

Q2 A lot of the mass of the filing cabinet is concentrated in the top drawer. So, when the drawer is fully pulled out, the centre of mass could move beyond the edge of the base, making the cabinet unstable.

Q3 C, because it has the widest base and lowest centre of mass.

Q4 The weight acts at the centre of mass = 40 cm from the pivot. The leg is 80 – 5 = 75 cm from the pivot.
Anticlockwise moments = Clockwise moments
$40 \text{ N} \times 0.4 \text{ m} = F \times 0.75 \text{ m}$
$16 \text{ Nm} = F \times 0.75 \text{ m}$
$16 \div 0.75 = F$
F = **21.3 N**

Page 80 — Circular Motion

Q1 D — a change in velocity

Q2 a) and b)

Q3 a) Yes. It is continually changing direction, so it must be changing velocity — accelerating.

b) The following statements should be ticked:
"If a body is accelerating then there must be a resultant force acting on it."
"If there is no resultant force acting on a body then it carries on moving in a straight line at the same speed."

c) Centripetal force

d) A runner running round a circular track — Friction
A satellite in orbit round the Earth — Gravity
The seats at the ends of the spokes of a spinning fairground ride — Tension

Q4 a) greater
b) smaller
c) 1617 N

Page 81 — Satellites

Q1 a) A geosynchronous satellite is in a **high** orbit over the Earth's **equator**.

b)

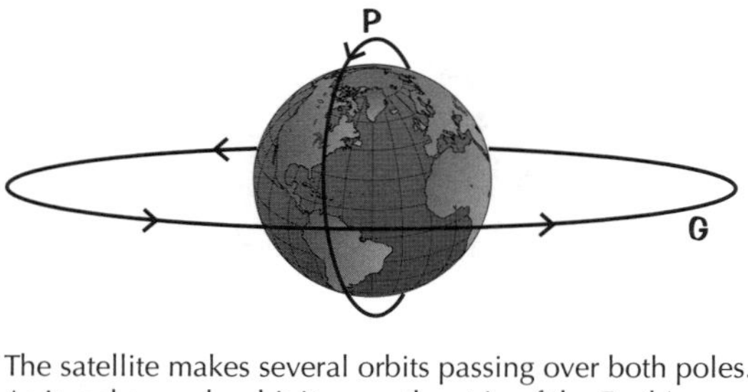

Q2a) The satellite makes several orbits passing over both poles. As it makes each orbit it scans the strip of the Earth's surface beneath it. Because the Earth is rotating beneath it, it can eventually cover the whole surface.

b) E.g. espionage, search and rescue, weather forecasting.

c) i) True
ii) True
iii) False
iv) False

d) No. The fact that they orbit the Earth shows that the Earth's gravity is exerting a force on them.

Q3 a) E.g. so that it is always in the same position relative to satellite dishes on the Earth's surface.

b) 24 hours

c) The signals from the satellites would interfere with each other.

Pages 82-83 — Gravity and Orbits

Q1 a) gravity, orbit, distance
b) Planets closer to the Sun move faster.

Q2a) and b)

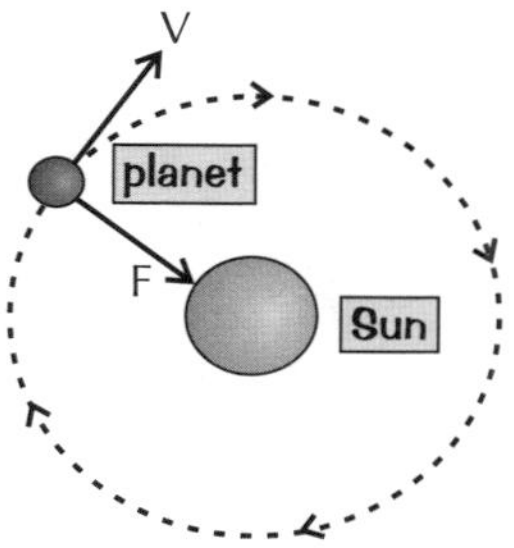

Q3a) i) D
ii) B

b) The distance between the comet and the Sun changes. So the force of gravity changes — making the comet orbit at different speeds.

Q4 a) C

b) Geostationary satellites need to take longer to orbit the Earth (24 hours rather than the few hours needed by polar satellites).

Q5 a) The force of gravity becomes a quarter as strong.

b) i) Distance is five times as great, so the gravitational force will be $1/5^2 = 1/25$ as strong. Gravitational force = 1/25 of 250 N = 250 ÷ 25 = **10 N**.

ii) Distance is halved, so the gravitational force will be $1/0.5^2 = 1 \div 0.25 = 4$ times as strong. Gravitational force = 4 × 250 N = **1000 N**.

Section Seven — Generating Electricity

Pages 84-85 — Magnetic Fields

Q1 a) north
b) south
c) north

Q2 a)

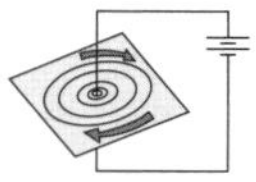

b) The circular magnetic fields around opposite sides of the loop reinforce each other in the centre.

E.g.

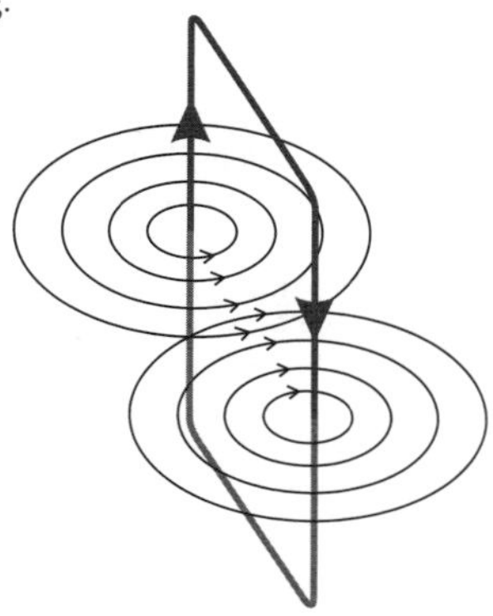

Q3 a) False. The field **outside** a solenoid is like a bar magnet's.

b) False. Iron is magnetically soft and will lose its magnetism when the current is switched off.

c) False. More turns increase the strength of the field.

d) True

Section Seven — Generating Electricity

Q4 a) and **b)**

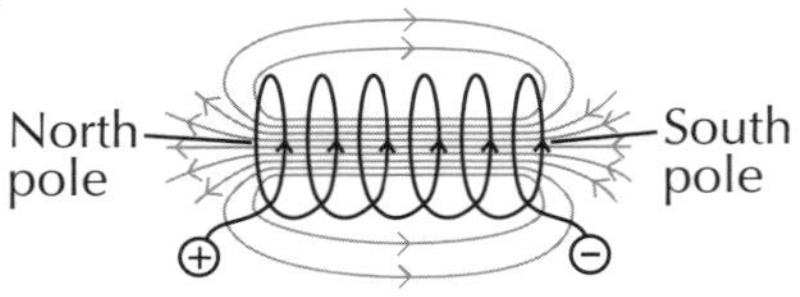

c) The iron would be attracted towards the solenoid.
d) i) Away from the coil.
ii) Any two from: turn the bar magnet round, reverse the direction of the current, wind the coil the opposite way round.
Q5 a) Magnetically hard materials keep their magnetism when the current is switched off. You wouldn't be able to drop the objects that the electromagnet had picked up.
b) Reversing the current in both will reverse the poles of both, so they will still repel each other.

Page 86 — The Motor Effect

Q1 magnetic, field, permanent, magnets, force, current, stronger, angle
Q2 a) Out of the paper (towards the reader).
b) By reversing the direction of the current. / By turning the magnets the other way round (reversing the magnetic field).
c) The magnetic fields of the permanent magnets and the current-carrying wire interact — producing a force.
Q3 a) B
b) i) Reverse the direction of the current in the bar. Reverse the polarity of the horseshoe magnet.
ii) Use a stronger horseshoe magnet. Use a bigger current in the bar.

Page 87 — The Simple Electric Motor

Q1 A, B, C and D.
Q2 The split-ring commutator reverses the direction of the current every half turn by swapping the contacts to the DC supply.
Q3 By reversing the polarity of the magnets. By reversing the direction of the current.
Q4 E.g. the axle of the electric motor could be used to turn a (large) pulley wheel, around which the lift cables would wind or unwind to raise or lower the lift.
Q5 a) Downwards (by using Fleming's Left-Hand Rule).
b) To make the motor more efficient. (Having curved pole pieces means that the coil experiences the full strength of the magnetic field for longer.)

Page 88 — Generators

Q1 magnetic field, current, slip, brushes, direction, half
Q2 The slip rings reverse the direction of the current supplied to an external circuit every half turn.
The slip rings enable the current to enter and leave the coils of the generator while it is turning.
Q3 As the bicycle goes more slowly it turns the dynamo more slowly and so a smaller voltage is induced. This means a smaller current flows through the bulb and the light gets dimmer.
Q4 a) D
b) B
c) A

Pages 89-90 — Transformers

Q1
1. A source of alternating voltage is applied to the primary coil.
2. An alternating current flows in the primary coil.
3. This causes a rapidly changing magnetic field in the iron core.
4. The changing magnetic field induces an alternating voltage in the secondary coil.
5. An alternating current can flow in a circuit connected to the secondary coil.

Q2 a) When a current flows in the left-hand coil it generates a magnetic field, inducing a current in the right-hand coil and causing the needle of the ammeter to deflect. Since a current is only induced when the magnetic field changes, the deflection only occurs when the current is switched on or off.
b) You could put an iron core through the two coils / add more coils / add more cells to the battery etc. Any of these would make the magnetic field stronger and therefore cause bigger deflections on the ammeter.
Q3 a) False
b) False
c) True
d) False
Q4 The voltage must decrease by a factor of 10 (from 230 V to 23 V), so the number of turns must also decrease by a factor of 10 — from 2000 to **200 turns**.
Alternatively, use the equation:

$$\frac{V_s}{V_p}=\frac{N_s}{N_p},\ \frac{23}{230}=\frac{N_s}{2000},\ N_s=\frac{2000\times 23}{230}=\mathbf{200\ turns.}$$

Q5 The number of turns increases by a factor of 40 so the voltage will also increase by a factor of 40. So the input voltage would need to be 10 000 ÷ 40 = **250 V**.
Alternatively, use the equation:

$$\frac{V_p}{V_s}=\frac{N_p}{N_s},\ \frac{V_p}{10\ 000}=\frac{100}{4000},\ V_p=\frac{10\ 000\times 100}{4000}=\mathbf{250\ V.}$$

Q6 a) B
b) It's used for safety. It allows you to use a shaver without it being physically connected to the mains. If you touch the live part of the shaver, it won't be connected to earth — this minimises the risk of electrocution.
Q7 a) The transformers are not 100% efficient, and the resistance of the cables causes energy to be lost as heat.
b) Substituting V = I × R into P = I × V, P = I × (I × R), so $P = I^2 \times R$.
c) It reduces the current (proportionally, assuming it's 100% efficient).
d) i) $I=\frac{P}{V},\ I=\frac{1\ 000\ 000\ W}{250\ V}=\mathbf{4000\ A.}$
ii) $I=\frac{1\ 000\ 000\ W}{250\ 000\ V}=\mathbf{4\ A.}$
e) It's much more efficient to transmit power at low current, because the power lost as heat is proportional to the square of the current ($P = I^2 \times R$). A way of reducing the current is to transmit the power at high voltages, since P = I × V. In order to do this, the National Grid uses step-up transformers at power stations to raise the voltage. Step-down transformers are used to bring the voltage back down to safe levels for homes and businesses.

Section Eight — Wave Behaviour

Page 91 — Nuclear Power

Q1 a) The heat energy in the reactor is carried away by (CO_2) gas. The hot gas heats water, turning it into steam, which turns a turbine, generating electricity.

b) i) They absorb excess neutrons (so they can't go on to cause fission). They are raised and lowered into the reactor to control the rate of fission.

ii) boron

c) To stop radiation escaping.

Q2 a) e.g. a nuclear bomb

b) The reaction is uncontrolled / much faster.

Q3 A single plutonium nucleus absorbs a slow-moving neutron. This nucleus then splits and produces other neutrons. These neutrons are absorbed by other plutonium nuclei. These nuclei split, producing even more neutrons, which can then cause even more nuclei to split. This is a chain reaction.

Page 92 — Nuclear Power and Fusion

Q1 a) Because it stays dangerously radioactive for an extremely long time (hundreds of years).

b) E.g. Place the waste in thick metal canisters, then put the canisters in a very deep hole and fill the hole with concrete.

Q2 a) True

b) False — A nuclear **fusion** reaction releases more energy than a nuclear fission reaction (for the same mass).

c) False — Fusion reactors will produce **very little** radioactive waste (if they can be made to work).

d) False — **No** experimental fusion reactors are generating electricity yet.

Q3 a) One of: extremely high temperatures / high densities. (Fusible nuclei also need to be present.)

b) i) The hydrogen needs to be at such a high temperature that any physical container would vaporise.

ii) By containing the hydrogen in a magnetic field.

c) So far they need more energy input (to get up to the right temperature) than the amount of energy they can produce.

d) Because it'd be safer, cheaper and much more efficient than many current electricity generating methods (if the engineering problems associated with high temperatures were removed). It would have the potential to generate lots of electricity with little pollution and no reliance on limited fuel reserves.

Section Eight — Wave Behaviour

Page 93 — Images

Q1 a) In a real image, the rays from the object actually pass through the image (so it can be projected onto a screen). In a virtual image, the rays only appear to have come from the location of the image.

b) i) virtual

ii) real

iii) virtual

c) You need to give its size, say whether it is upright or inverted and real or virtual.

Q2

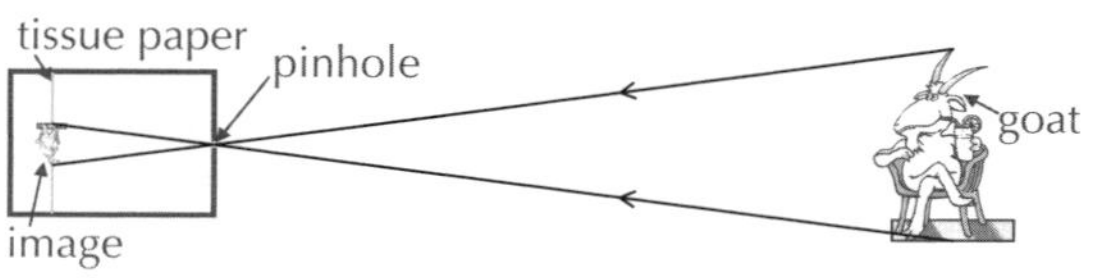

Q3 a) The wall does reflect light, just not evenly like a mirror. Light being reflected off the wall into our eyes is what allows us to see the wall.

b) angle of incidence = angle of reflection

c) it bends / changes direction

d) D — Refraction is caused by light changing speed as it enters another medium.

Pages 94-95 — Mirrors

Q1 a)

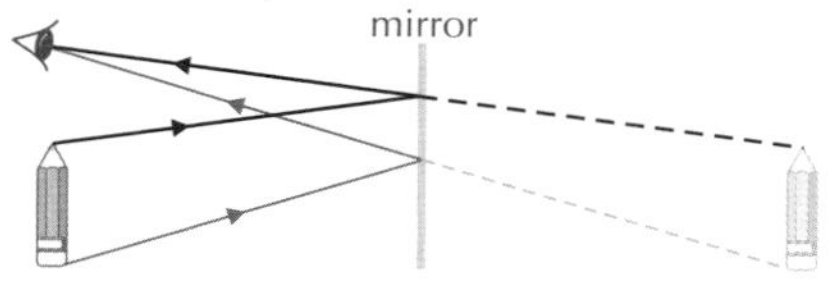

b) virtual

Q2

	Description	Behaviour of parallel rays shining on mirror
Concave mirror	Reflective on inside of curve.	Reflected light converges.
Convex mirror	Reflective on outside of curve.	Reflected light diverges.

Q3

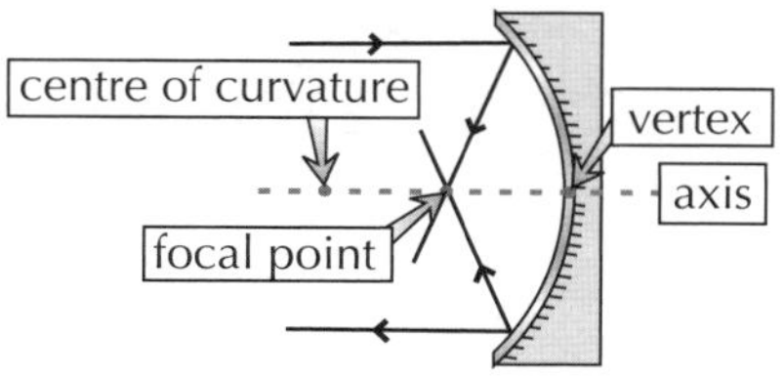

Q4 a) An incident ray passing through the focal point is reflected so that it is parallel to the axis.

b)

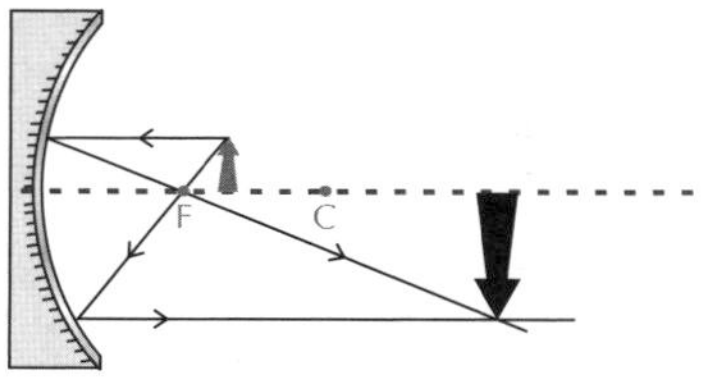

c) i) As the object is moved past C the image becomes smaller than the object. (At C, the object and image are the same size.)

ii) The image gets nearer to the mirror and passes C at the same time as the object.

Q5 a) False

b) True

c) True

d) False

Q6 a) E.g. a road safety mirror to help people to see further round a corner; a security measure in a shop, so the shop keeper can see round corners from the till.

b) They give a wider field of view than a plane mirror.

Q7 a) Because the focal point of a convex mirror is behind the mirror.

b) incident, extended, parallel to the axis

Q8

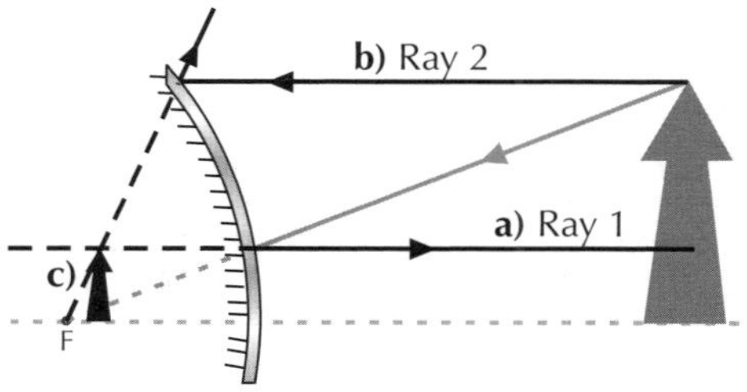

Section Eight — Wave Behaviour

Pages 96-97 — Refractive Index and Snell's Law

Q1 a)

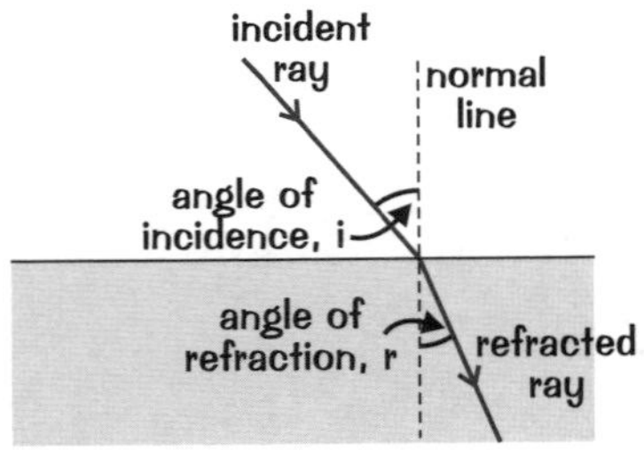

b) n = sin i / sin r

Q2 n = sin 30 ÷ sin 22 = **1.3**.

Q3 a)

i	r	sin i	sin r
10.0°	8.3°	0.17	0.14
20.0°	16.4°	0.34	0.28
30.0°	24.8°	0.50	0.42
40.0°	32.3°	0.64	0.53
50.0°	39.8°	0.77	0.64
60.0°	46.2°	0.87	0.72

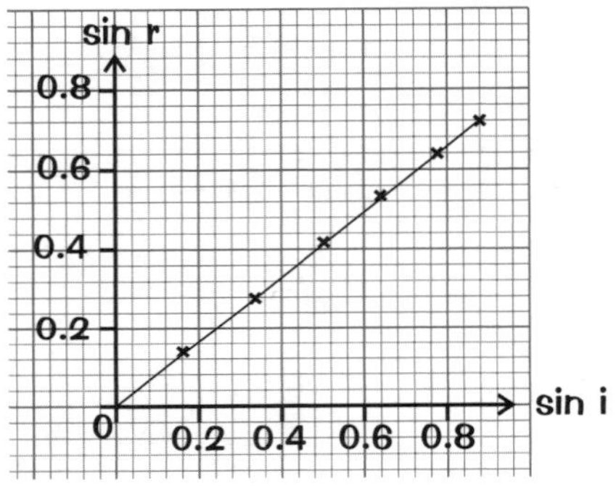

b) Gradient = sin r / sin i.
n = sin i / sin r and so 1/n = sin r / sin i, which is the same formula as the gradient.

c) Gradient = 0.83.
Therefore n = 1 ÷ 0.83 = **1.2**.

Q4 a) n = sin i / sin r, so 1.514 = sin 45 ÷ sin r.
Therefore sin r = sin 45 ÷ 1.514 = 0.467.
Hence r = $\sin^{-1}$ (0.467) = **27.8°**.

b) This is a higher refractive index, so the violet light must be travelling more slowly.

c) First calculate the angle of refraction for violet light. sin r = sin 45 ÷ 1.529 = 0.463. So r = $\sin^{-1}$(0.463) = 27.6°.
The angle of refraction for red light = 27.8°. The angle θ will be the difference between these two angles = 27.8 – 27.6 = **0.2°**.

Q5 a) i) The speed increases.
ii) The angle of refraction is **greater than** the angle of incidence.

b) The angle of refraction would be 90°.

c) The light is totally internally reflected — all of the light reflects and there is no refraction.

d) sin C = n_r / n_i = 1.337 ÷ 1.498 = 0.893 (3 s.f.).
C = $\sin^{-1}$(0.893) = **63°** (to the nearest degree).

Pages 98-99 — Lenses

Q1 a) Medium 1 is glass. Medium 2 is air.
b) Because light is refracted away from the normal as it goes from a more dense medium into a less dense medium.

Q2 a)

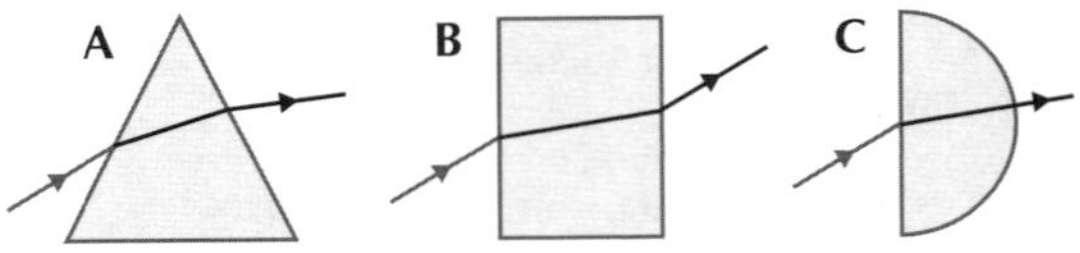

b) White light leaving Prism A would be split into a spectrum making a rainbow effect.

c) White light. A rectangular prism has parallel boundaries, so although different colours are refracted by different amounts as they enter, they're bent back by the same amount as they leave.

d) red

Q3 a) diverging
b) W = incident
X = converging
Y = parallel
Z = focal point

c) The following statements should be ticked:
Any ray passing along the axis
Any ray passing through the centre of the lens

Q4 a)

Distance from lens to object	Distance from lens to image	Type of image	Size of image
Greater than 2F	Between 2F and F	Real, inverted	Smaller than object
Equal to 2F	Equal to 2F	Real, inverted	Equal to object
Between 2F and F	Greater than 2F	Real, inverted	Larger than object
Less than F	Greater than 2F	Virtual, upright	Larger than object

b) i) The image will be 1 cm high.
ii) The image will be 5 cm away from the lens on the opposite side from the object.

Q5 a) i) upright
ii) on the same side
iii) virtual

b) C – 10.2 cm

Q6

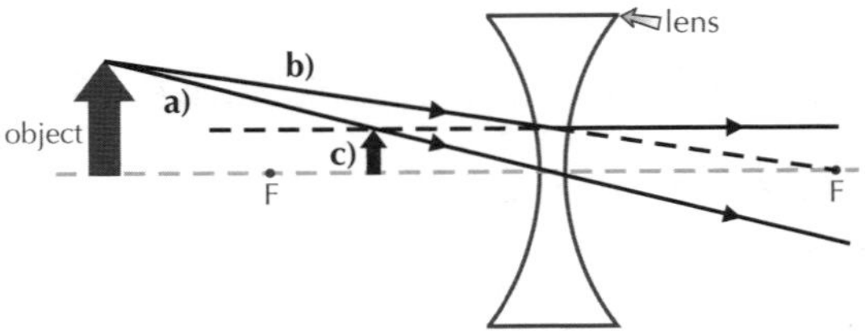

Pages 100-101 — Uses — Magnification and Cameras

Q1 a) Just less than one focal length in front of the lens.
b) The image will be a virtual image.
c) Try to display it on a screen. If you can capture it on a screen it's real. If you can't it's virtual.

Q2 a) Magnification = image height ÷ object height
b) image height ÷ object height = 6 ÷ 1.5 = **4**.
c) 0.002 = image height ÷ object height.
0.002 = 2 ÷ object height.
So height of tree = 2 ÷ 0.002 = 1000 cm = **10 m**.

Section Eight — Wave Behaviour

Q3 The ray diagram should look like this.

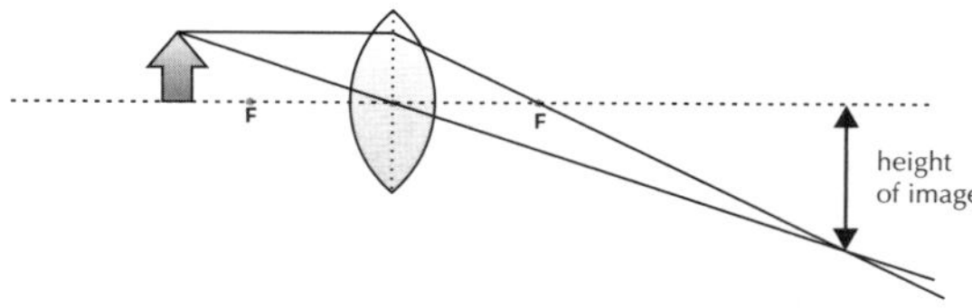

To actual size, the image is 2.3 cm tall (accept between 2 and 2.6 cm). Therefore magnification = 2.3 cm ÷ 1 cm = **2.3**. (You need to draw the ray diagram really carefully to get the right answer.)

Q4 a) The magnification is **less than 1**.
The image is **real**.
The image is **upside down**.

b)

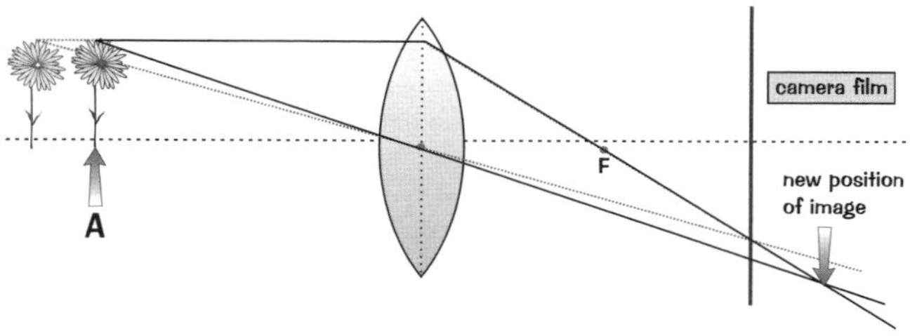

c) Move the lens further away from the film.

Q5 a) The magnification is **more than 1.**
The image is **real.**
The image is **upside down.**

b) You need to put the film in upside down (so that the image produces a picture that is the right way up).

c) You would have to move the film closer to the lens (which has the same effect as moving the flower closer to the lens in question 4).

Page 102 — Interference of Waves

Q1 a)

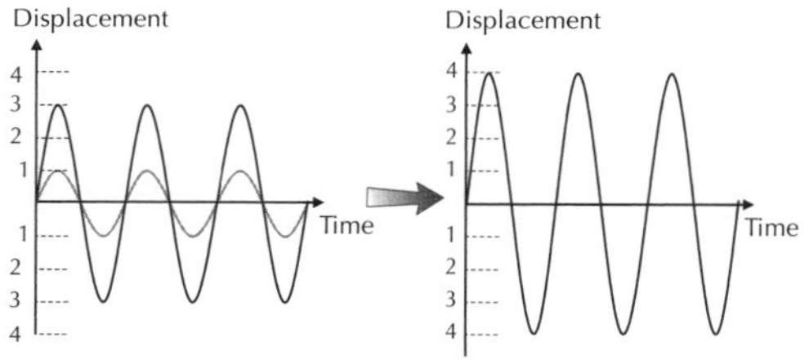

This is **constructive** interference.

b)

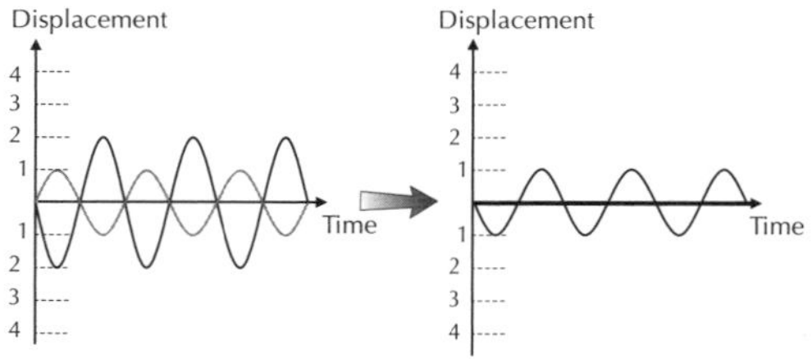

This is **destructive** interference.

Q2 a) The two sound waves must be destructively interfering. The combined wave has a smaller amplitude and so sounds quieter.

b) Caleb might have heard patches of loud sound where the waves were constructively interfering and much softer sounds where the waves were destructively interfering.

Q3 a) You would see fringes of light and dark on the screen.

b) The wavelength of light waves is much smaller than the wavelength of sound.

c) B

Page 103 — Diffraction Patterns and Polarisation

Q1 a) True

b) False

c) True

d) False

Q2 a) The laser light must already be polarised. The glasses will only let the light through if they are 'lined up' with their plane of vibration.

b) The glasses wouldn't block the light because normal light is unpolarised so light will still be seen on the screen.

c) Reflected light is partially polarised, so rotating the glasses would partially block the light (not as much as the laser).

d) On a sunny day, reflected light from a wet road surface can dazzle drivers. Polaroid sunglasses can reduce the light intensity from the reflections without reducing the overall light intensity as much.

Q3 Light from every point in the circular hole diffracts. This gives many overlapping waves, which cause a pattern of bright regions (where the waves interfere constructively) and dark regions (where the waves interfere destructively).

Pages 104-105 — Sound Waves

Q1 C, A, D, B.

Q2 a) air

b) It travels faster through a solid.

Q3 vibrate, high, low, amplitude, quiet

Q4 a) 30 Hz

b) 5 Hz, 630 Hz, 8 kHz, 21 kHz, 400 kHz, 3 MHz

Q5 a) a reflected sound wave

b) The soft surfaces in her bedroom absorb the sound vibrations better, so less sound is reflected around the room.

Q6 a) It gets quieter and eventually stops. Because sound is a vibration passed from molecule to molecule, it cannot be transmitted through a vacuum.

b) The foam prevents the sound from being transmitted through the solid surface that the clock is placed on.

Q7 a) a sine wave / sinusoidal

b) 8 divisions = 0.04 seconds

c) 1/0.04 = 25 Hz

d) E.g.

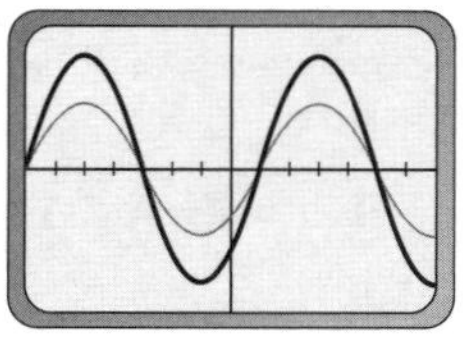

Q8 By the shape of the waveform (e.g. a sine wave, a sawtooth wave, a square wave etc.)

Page 106 — Ultrasound

Q1 a) Ultrasound is sound with a higher frequency than we can hear.

b) Electrical devices can be set to produce electrical oscillations at the required frequency. These can be converted into mechanical vibrations (i.e. sound waves).

Q2 Sean needs to set the time base on the oscilloscope so that each square on the screen corresponds to a much shorter interval of time.

Q3 a) The boundary between the girder and air and then another boundary between the air and the rest of the girder.

Section Nine — Circuits and Logic Gates

b) 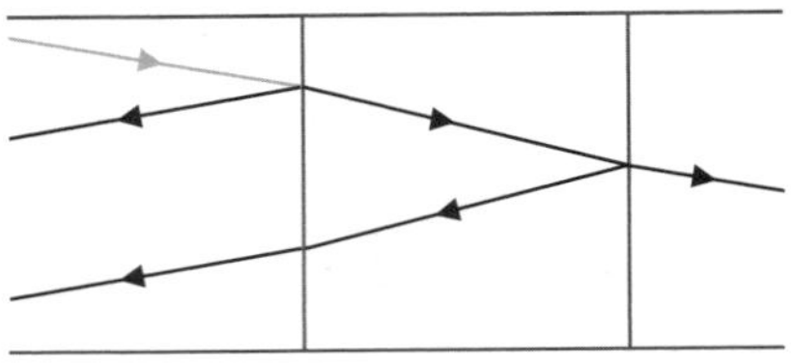

c) The scanner detects how long the echoes take to return. If you know the speed of sound in the medium you can work out how far the pulse has travelled using distance = speed × time.

Page 107 — Uses of Ultrasound

Q1 a) While no one can be certain that ultrasound is harmless, X-rays are likely to harm the foetus.

b) Sample answer: A beam of **ultrasound** is sent into the mother's womb. Inside the **uterus** the beam hits the **boundary** between the **amniotic fluid** and the body tissues of the **foetus**. The beam is partly **reflected** at this boundary. The reflected waves are **processed** by computer to produce an **image** of the foetus on a **monitor**.

c) E.g. dentists can use ultrasound to clean teeth.

Q2 a) Use $v = f \times \lambda$ to find the speed of sound in the crack.
$v = 28\ 000 \times 0.05$
$v = 1400$ m/s

b) The distance the pulse travelled is given by
$d = v \times t$
$d = 1400 \times (130 \times 10^{-6})$
$d = 0.182$ m
This is twice the width of the crack, so the width of the crack is:
$0.182 \div 2 = 0.091$ m = 9.1 cm.

Section Nine — Circuits and Logic Gates

Page 108 — Potential Dividers

Q1 a) A potential divider consists of a **pair of resistors**.

b) The higher the value of a resistor the **bigger** the voltage drop across it.

Q2 a) True

b) True

c) False

Q3 a) i) If the output voltage is too small you could increase it by **decreasing** the resistance of resistor $\mathbf{R_1}$.

ii) If the output voltage is too high you could decrease it by **increasing** the resistance of resistor $\mathbf{R_1}$ / **decreasing** the resistance of resistor $\mathbf{R_2}$.

b) hot, decreases

Q4 a) Equal resistors so V_{out} is half of 6 V = **3 V**.

b) $V_{out} = 6 \times \frac{10}{20+10} = 6 \times \frac{1}{3} = \mathbf{2\ V}$.

Q5 a) **7 V** (read across graph and down).

b) **0 Ω** (all the input voltage must drop across R_2).

c) **4 Ω**. (When V_{out} is 50% of input voltage, resistors are equal. 50% of input voltage = 3 V. From graph R_1 = 4 Ω when output = 3 V.)

Pages 109-110 — Diodes and Rectification

Q1 Semiconductor — conducts electricity but not as well as a conductor
n-type semiconductor — has extra free electrons
p-type semiconductor — has empty spaces called 'holes' where electrons are missing
Diode — allows a current to flow in one direction only

Q2 a) i) True
ii) False
iii) False
iv) True
v) True

b) ii) **Diodes** have a low resistance in one direction and high resistance in the other.

iii) n-type semiconductors and p-type semiconductors both contain impurities.

Q3 a) i) 'Rectification' means turning AC into DC.

ii) Many electrical devices, e.g. radios, need direct current.

b) half-wave rectification

c) four

Q4 To create p-type semiconductors with free holes or n-type semiconductors with extra free electrons.

Q5 Free electrons move into the p-type semiconductor, and free holes move into the n-type semiconductor. These recombine and form an insulating region where there are no holes or free electrons.

Q6 In Circuit A the potential difference gives free electrons in the n-type semiconductor enough energy to cross the insulating region to the p-type semiconductor. The electrons and holes move across the junction and a current flows in the circuit. In Circuit B the potential difference is trying to 'pull' the electrons away from the junction rather than across it — so no electrons move across the junction and no current flows.

Q7 a) 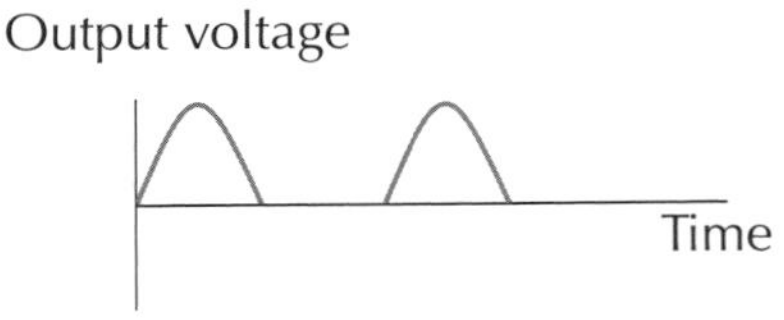

b) 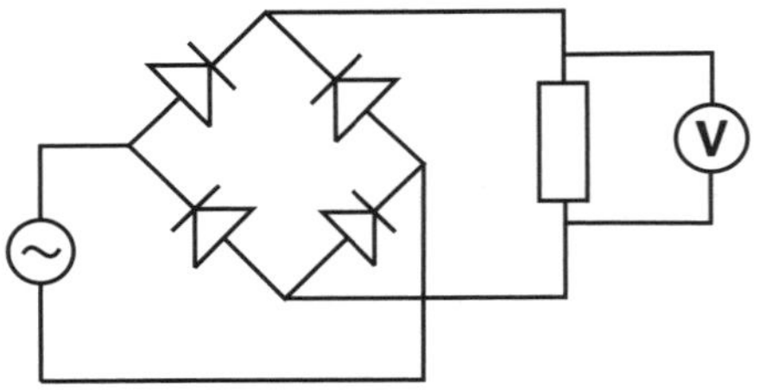

Page 111 — Capacitors

Q1 E.g. connect a voltage across it and allow the capacitor to charge until no more current flows / the voltage across it equals the voltage of the power supply (connect an ammeter in series or a voltmeter in parallel to see when this happens).

Q2 a) i) True
ii) False

b) i) A capacitor can be used to store electric **charge**.

Q3 a) Many electronic devices are very sensitive to input voltage / need a smooth (i.e. steady) voltage.

b) It flows from the power supply and divides. Some goes through the component and some goes to charge the capacitor.

c) No current flows to or from the voltage supply. Current flows from the capacitor and through the component. The capacitor discharges.

d) Approximately the same current flows through the component all the time: sometimes from the power supply, sometimes from the capacitor.

Q4
1. Initially the capacitor **has no charge stored**, so the voltage across it is **small** and the output voltage is **small**.
2. Charge flows into the capacitor so the voltage across it gradually **increases** and the voltage across the resistor **decreases**.
3. As this happens the output voltage gradually **rises**.

Section Ten — Particles in Action

Page 112 — Logic Gates

Q1 a) digital
b) inverter
Q2 a) AND gate
b) NAND gate
c) OR gate
d) NOR gate
e) NOT gate
Q3 NOR gate AND gate NAND gate NOT gate

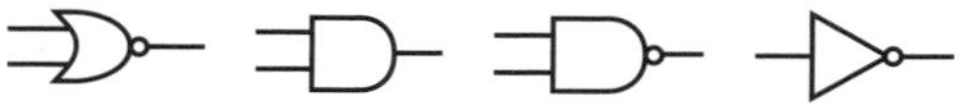

Q4 a)

A	B	Output
0	0	**1**
0	1	1
1	0	1
1	1	**0**

b) AND, NOT (must be in that order)
Q5 a) NOR
b) NOT
c) AND
d) NAND

Page 113 — Using Logic Gates

Q1 a)

A	B	C	D	Output
0	0	**1**	**1**	**1**
1	0	**0**	**1**	**0**
0	1	**1**	**0**	**0**
1	1	**0**	**0**	**0**

b) Yes

Q2 a)

A	B	C	D	Output
0	0	0	**0**	**0**
0	0	1	**0**	**1**
0	1	0	**1**	**1**
0	1	1	**1**	**1**
1	0	0	**1**	**1**
1	0	1	**1**	**1**
1	1	0	**1**	**1**
1	1	1	**1**	**1**

b) Yes
c) Yes
Q3 a) i) The output at B becomes 0 (because the inputs to the top NOR gate are 1 0). This means the inputs to the bottom NOR gate are now 0 0 so the main output is 1 and the warning light comes on.
ii) Nothing happens. / The light stays on.
When S goes to 0 again, the inputs to the top logic gate become 0 1 (remember that the main output is still 1) so the output at B stays at 0 and the inputs to the bottom NOR gate are unchanged.
b) Set input R to **1** briefly — this changes the inputs to the bottom NOR gate to 0 1, giving an output of 0.

Page 114 — LEDs and Relays in Logic Circuits

Q1 a) True
b) False
c) True
Q2 a) E.g. any two from: logic circuits don't usually supply much current — not enough for an ordinary bulb / LEDs use only low power / LEDs last longer / LEDs can give (various) coloured lights.
b) E.g. to ensure that the current is small — a large current might damage the LED.
Q3 a) Logic circuits can only supply small currents.
b) The logic circuit could be connected in a low current circuit to a relay. The relay can then switch the high current circuit off or on.
Q4 a) When the output from the logic circuit is 1, current flows in the coil of the electromagnet, which attracts the iron contact on a rocker switch. The rocker pivots and closes the contacts in the high current circuit. When the output from the logic circuit is 0, current stops flowing in the electromagnet's coil and so it is no longer magnetised, the rocker falls back to open the switch, and the high current circuit is broken again.
b) E.g. It is safer because the user is isolated from the high current circuit.

Section Ten — Particles in Action

Page 115 — Kinetic Theory and Temperature in Gases

Q1 ice, 0 °C, water, 100 °C, absolute, 0 K, -273 °C
Q2 a) K
b) faster
c) kinetic, proportional
Q3 a) 276 K
b) 483 K
c) 228 K
d) 273 K
Q4 a) -273 °C
b) 27 °C
c) 367 °C
d) -243 °C
Q5 a) kinetic energy = $\frac{1}{2}mv^2$
b) 277 °C = 550 K, 827 °C = 1100 K. The temperature is doubled (1100 = 2 × 550), so the kinetic energy must also be doubled. $1.14 \times 10^{20} \times 2 = \mathbf{2.28 \times 10^{20}}$ **J**.
c) The particles of air freshener will have less kinetic energy on a cold day, so the average speed of the particles will be lower than on a hot day.

Page 116 — Kinetic Theory and Pressure in Gases

Q1 a) B, D
b) When gas particles collide with the side of a container they exert a force on the container, creating an outward pressure.
Q2 a) B
b) Because the boiling point of water (which is being used to heat the gas) is 100 °C.

Section Ten — Particles in Action

c)

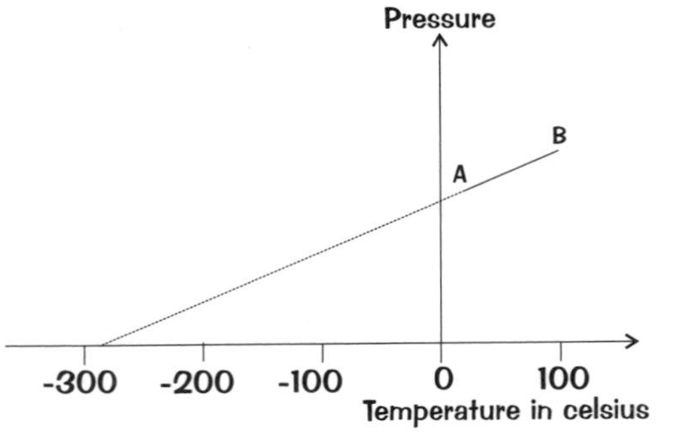

d) -273 °C

Q3 a) The pressure has fallen. The temperature has risen.

b)

$$\frac{P_1V_1}{T_1} = \frac{P_2V_2}{T_2} \Rightarrow \frac{6\times5}{277} = \frac{1\times V_2}{293} \Rightarrow V_2 = \frac{6\times5\times293}{1\times277} = \mathbf{31.7\ cm^3}$$

Pages 117-118 — Particles in Atoms

Q1 a) alpha — 3, beta — 2, gamma — 1

b) The more penetrating it is, the less ionising it is (e.g. alpha particles are stopped by paper but are strongly ionising).

c) i) E.g. paper / skin

ii) E.g. thin metal

Q2 a) neutron, proton, stays the same

b) proton, neutron, decreases by 1

c) element, atomic/proton

Q3 a) more

b) charge, ionise

c) radioactive

Q4 a) beta-plus decay

b) 14, 5

c) Positrons are annihilated as soon as they meet an electron.

Q5 a) Atoms with the same atomic number but different mass numbers.

b) unstable

c) neutron-rich

d) They have too many protons — the positive charges repel each other.

e) beta-plus decay

f) alpha decay

Q6 a) Very heavy atoms with more than 82 protons.

b) $^{224}_{88}\text{Ra} \rightarrow ^{220}_{86}\text{Rn} + ^{4}_{2}\text{alpha}$

c) By emitting gamma radiation.

Q7 a) light nuclei

b) Neutron absorption often makes nuclei unstable and causes them to emit gamma radiation.

Pages 119-120 — Fundamental and Other Particles

Q1 a) A particle that cannot be broken down into smaller particles.

b) electron, positron

c) Yes, by smashing particles together at very high speed.

Q2 B and E should be ticked.

Q3 Electron — fundamental particle, charge -1
Down-quark — relative charge -1/3
Proton — relative mass 1, charge +1
Neutron — made up of two down-quarks and one up-quark
Positron — fundamental particle, charge +1
Up-quark — relative mass 1/3, relative charge 2/3

Q4 proton, electron, beta-minus decay

Q5 a) accelerated, energy, energy, matter, matter

b) i) same mass

ii) opposite charge

iii) positron

c) No. The proton is not a fundamental particle, but made up of quarks, so an antiproton would also be made up of quarks.

d) -1

Q6 a)

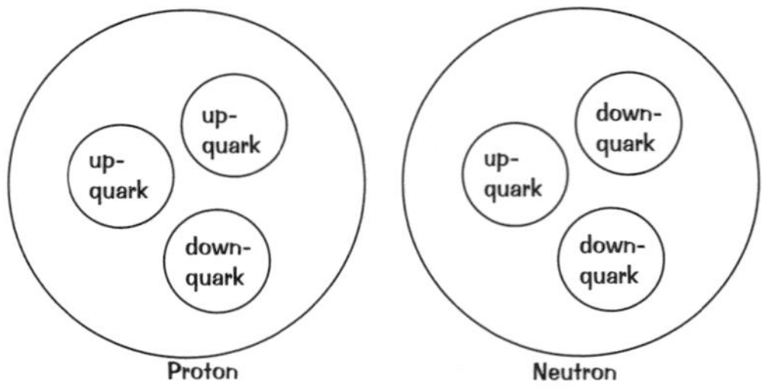

b) neutron, positron

c) An up-quark is changed into a down-quark.

Pages 121-122 — Electron Beams

Q1 a)

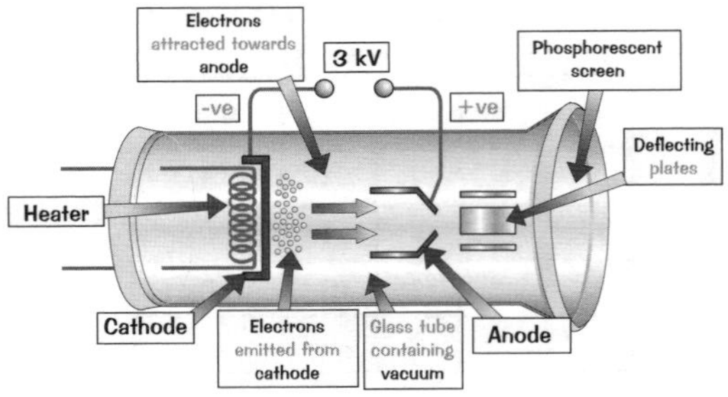

b) Heating the cathode gives more energy to its electrons. Once they have enough energy they 'boil off'.

c) i) the anode

ii) the deflecting plates

d) Chemicals in the screen absorb the electron and emit light, causing the screen to glow.

Q2 a) Current is the rate of flow of electrons/charge.

b) 0.004 C

c) $0.004 \div 1.6 \times 10^{-19} = \mathbf{2.5 \times 10^{16}}$

Q3 a) attracted to, repelled by

b) Y-plates, X-plates

Q4

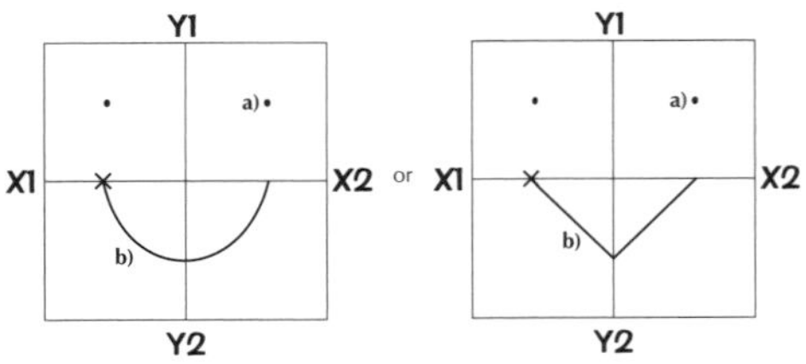

Q5 a), b)

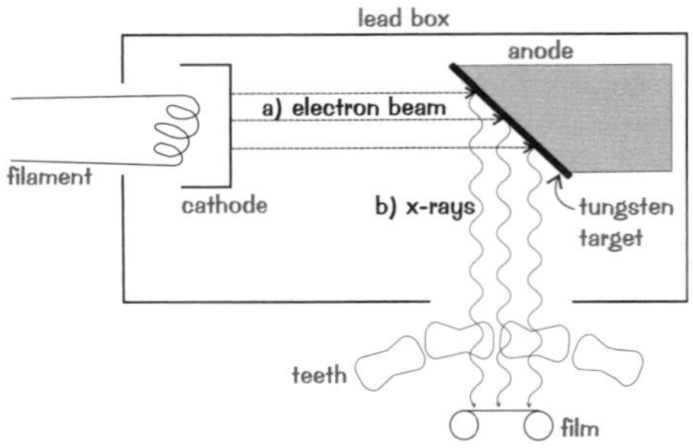

c) Some of the kinetic energy from the electrons is converted into X-rays.

Section Eleven — Medical Physics

Q6 a) charge on the plates — increase
mass of the plates — no change
charge on the particles — increase
mass of the particles — decrease
speed of the particles — decrease

b) Particle accelerators are often too expensive for the scientists' own countries to buy on their own. By collaborating there are more scientists working on the problem and so the best solution will probably be found more quickly.

Section Eleven — Medical Physics

Pages 123-124 — Medical Uses of Light

Q1 a)

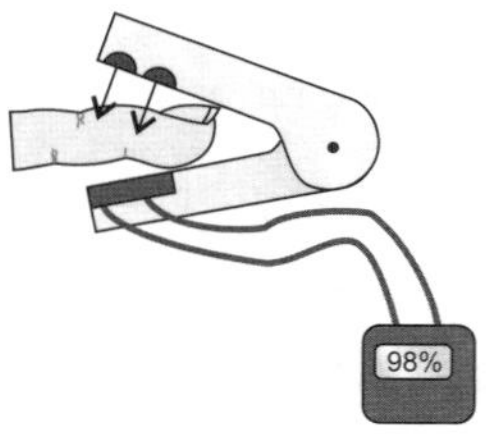

b) tissue, absorbed, reduced, calibrated

c) The ear lobe, because it is thin enough to allow the light beam to pass through it (and has a blood supply).

Q2 a) glass or perspex/plastic

b) If the tube is bent too much, the angle of incidence may be below the critical angle, allowing light to escape.

Q3 a) Surgery where a small hole is made and the operation carried out with small instruments and observed with an endoscope.

b) An endoscope contains two bundles of fibres — one to take light to the area of interest, and one to carry an image back.

c) Any two of: e.g. smaller cut made / less traumatic / patient in hospital for shorter time / cheaper

Q4 a) Reflection pulse oximetry reflects light off red blood cells, rather than shining light through them.

b) Oxyhaemoglobin is — bright red — and rich in oxygen. Reduced haemoglobin is — purply coloured — and doesn't contain much oxygen.

Pages 125-126 — Energy and Metabolic Rate

Q1 a) The rate at which the body transfers energy.

b) 7 kJ/min but accept anything between 4.5 and 14.

c) i) E.g. any three of: breathing / heartbeat / digestion / tissue repair / mental processes.

ii) The chemical potential energy in food.

Q2 a) The metabolic rate is lowest when the body is at rest — Ed's body is not at rest just after lunch because it's digesting the meal.

b) i) BMR measures the minimum amount of energy needed to keep all the body's essential processes working properly.

ii) Ed should go without food for 12 hours and then lie down so that he is fully at rest. His BMR is the amount of heat energy generated by his body over a certain time. If the experiment is repeated after he eats, the heat energy given out will be greater.

Q3 a) Metabolic rate = energy transferred/time. Rearranging, energy transferred = metabolic rate × time = 50 × 3 = **150 kJ**.

b) P.E. = mgh = 60 × 10 × 100 = 60 000 J = **60 kJ**.

c) The transfer of energy is not 100% efficient — some of the energy used by Denny will have been used by mechanisms within his body and some lost as heat.

Q4 a)

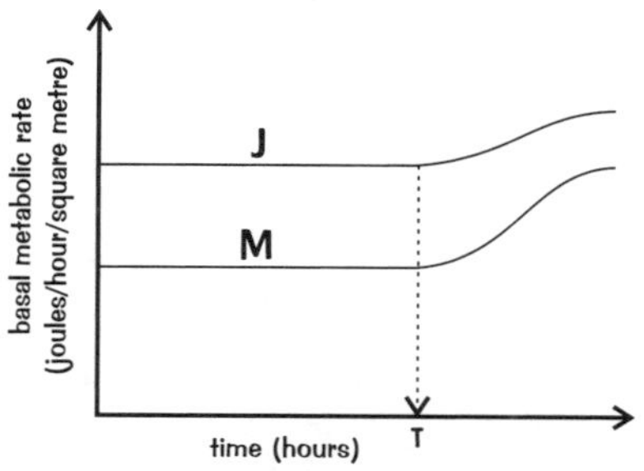

Children have a higher BMR than adults.

b) i) The room temperature may have gone down.

ii) Joanna's mum will have a larger body surface area so will lose heat faster. Her BMR will change faster than Joanna's to compensate.

Q5 a) i) It will dramatically reduce Chloe's BMR.

ii) Having a lower BMR means that her body will use less energy, so Chloe would need to eat less to maintain her weight.

b) Exercise uses up stored energy reserves (fat) and will increase Chloe's BMR, meaning that she uses energy faster.

Q6 In the tropical Indonesian climate, people don't need to use so much energy keeping their bodies warm, so have a lower BMR than people in the cooler European climate.

Page 127 — Electricity and the Body

Q1 a) EMG machines measure the small electrical signals in muscles.

b) i) The potential difference across a muscle cell membrane when the cell is at rest.

ii) An electrical signal that increases the potential of a muscle cell, making the cell contract.

c) +40 mV

Q2 a) The heart is a muscle containing four chambers — the atria at the top and the ventricles at the bottom.

b) An action potential passes through the atria making them contract. A fraction of a second later, another action potential passes through the ventricles making them contract too.

c) An ECG records the action potentials of the heart using electrodes stuck on the chest, arms and legs.

Q3 a)

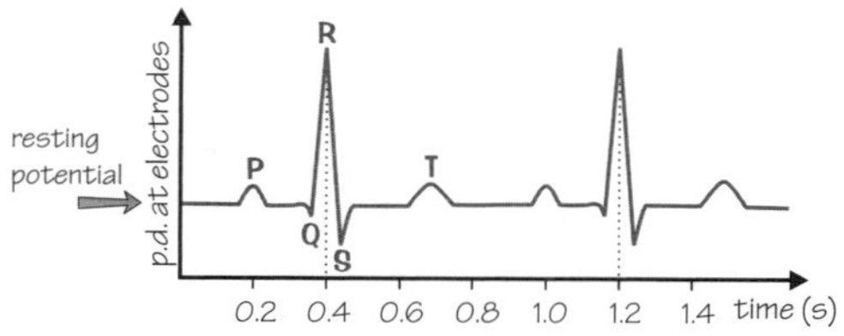

b) 0.8 s

c) frequency = 1 ÷ time period = 1 ÷ 0.8 = 1.25 Hz.
1.25 × 60 = **75 bpm**.

d) i) The contraction of the atria.

ii) The contraction of the ventricles and the relaxation of the atria.

iii) The relaxation of the ventricles.

Section Eleven — Medical Physics

Page 128 — Intensity of Radiation

Q1 a)

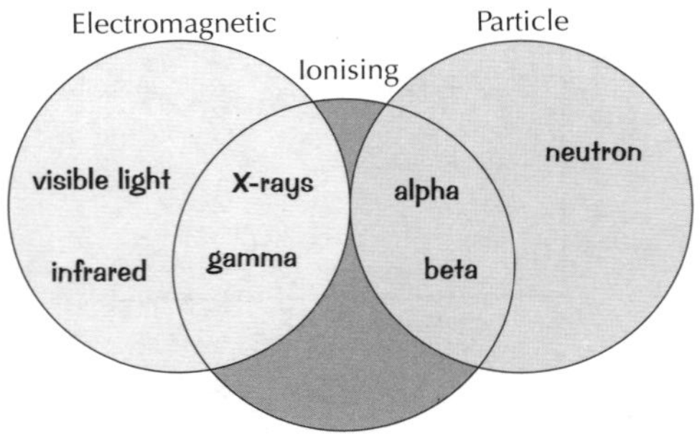

b) Radiation is energy emitted from a source.

Q2 a) Intensity is proportional to the inverse square of distance.

i) distance doubled, therefore Intensity = $8 \times 1/(2^2) = 8/4 = \mathbf{2\ W/m^2}$

ii) Intensity = $8 \times 1/(\frac{1}{2})^2 = \mathbf{32\ W/m^2}$

iii) Intensity = $8 \times 1/(4^2) = \mathbf{0.5\ W/m^2}$

b) **16 W/m²** (Intensity is directly proportional to power, so it will double.)

Q3 a) The lantern has a radius of 20 cm = 0.2 m
So, $4/3 \times \pi \times 0.2^2 = \mathbf{0.17\ m^2}$ (2 s.f.)

b) $I = P \div A = 0.8 \div 0.17 = \mathbf{4.7\ W/m^2}$

c) The intensity of the light reaching the outside surface will be lower because some light will be absorbed by the material of the lantern.

Page 129 — Nuclear Bombardment

Q1 a) i) A low energy neutron.

ii) A slow-moving, low energy neutron is fired at and absorbed by the uranium-235 nucleus.

b) The atoms have a larger proportion of neutrons than stable atoms with a similar atomic number.

c) E.g. tracers in medical diagnosis.

Q2 nucleus, proton, element, accelerator, cyclotron

Q3 a) $^{18}_{8}O + ^{1}_{1}p \longrightarrow ^{18}_{9}F + ^{1}_{0}n$ $\quad$ $^{14}_{7}N + ^{1}_{1}p \longrightarrow ^{11}_{6}C + ^{4}_{2}He$

b) i) positron

ii) PET scanning

iii) Hospitals may have their own facilities because the isotopes have a short half-life.

Page 130 — Momentum Conservation

Q1 a) i) total momentum = $m_n v_1$

ii) total momentum = $m_n v_3 + m_s v_4$

b) Conservation of momentum means that the total momentum before a collision is equal to the total momentum after the collision.
$m_n v_1 = m_n v_3 + m_s v_4$

Q2 a) i) momentum = $1 \times 2 = \mathbf{2}$

ii) momentum = $235 \times 0.1 = \mathbf{23.5}$

b) Momentum is conserved, so the momentum of the U-236 atom must equal the total momentum before the collision. $2 + 23.5 = \mathbf{25.5}$

Q3 a) i)

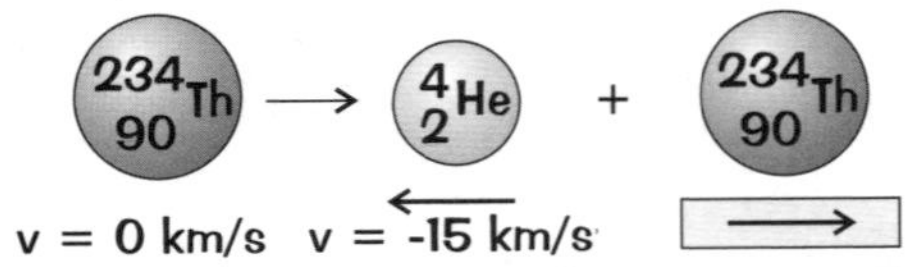

ii) The momentum before the collision was zero. For the total momentum after the collision to remain at zero, the particles must move in opposite directions.

b) $0 = 4 \times -15 + 234 \times v$.
Rearranging, $v = 60/234 = \mathbf{0.26\ km/s}$.

Q4 a) gamma rays, gamma rays, energy, velocities

b) The mass of the electron and the positron is converted into the energy of the gamma rays.

Page 131 — Medical Uses of Radiation

Q1 a) i) PET shows organ function while X-rays only show structure.

ii) Any one of: PET is much more expensive than X-rays./ PET gives a larger dose of radiation than X-rays.

b) E.g. any two of: Parkinson's, Alzheimer's, epilepsy, depression.

Q2
1. A positron-emitting radioactive isotope is added to a substance used by the body to make a radiotracer.
2. The patient is injected with the radiotracer.
3. The radiotracer moves through the body to the organs.
4. The radioisotope emits positrons.
5. The positrons collide with electrons and are annihilated, releasing gamma rays.
6. Detectors around the body record the position of the emitted gamma rays.
7. A computer builds up a map of radioactivity in the body.

Q3 a) i) metabolic activity

ii) Because more of the radioactive glucose is taken up by cells that are doing more work.

b) Cancer cells are dividing rapidly, so they show up as regions of very high metabolic activity.

c) PET scans expose patients to radiation, which increases the risk of cancer.

Q4 a) Radiotherapy can be used not to cure patients, but to relieve their suffering.

b) Any two of: by destroying them completely, by damaging them so they cannot stop dividing, by altering their genetic material.

Page 132 — Medical Research

Q1 Endoscope — keyhole surgery
ECG — monitoring heart conditions
PET — locating cancer cells
Antibiotic development — mutating bacteria

Q2 a) i) Because it has been shown to be effective for treating breast cancer in end-stage patients.

ii) E.g. unexpected side effects / untested on early-stage patients.

b) E.g. the disposal of the radioisotopes.

Q3 a) Drug companies recoup their development costs and make a profit by selling their patent drugs at a high price. If they don't make so much profit because patients are buying the generic drugs, they are less likely to invest in further drug development.

b) i) E.g. Poor drugs could get on to the market based on unsound testing regimes.

ii) E.g. one of: it gets drugs to where they are needed at an affordable cost / it can stem an epidemic, e.g. AIDS.

c) E.g. how soon should it be made available to everyone / should the testing be 'fast-tracked'.